Sunday Savers™

Activities to Make Learning Fun
For Sunbeams—Children Age 3

For each lesson you'll find two ways to teach:
. a cut and create activity, or
. an easy-handout poster

Home Activity: Let's listen to music together! Help me know what kind of music makes me feel happy and helps me think of Heavenly Father and Jesus.

Written by Mary H. Ross • Illustrated by Jennette Guymon-King

Introducing the Author and Illustrator, Creators of

The Following Series of Books and Printable CD-ROM Versions of Each Book

- **PRIMARY LESSON ACTIVITIES & HANDOUTS** (for manuals 1–7 & more): Sunday Savers: Nursery, Sunbeams, CTR-A and CTR-B (ages 4-7); Book of Mormon, D&C, New Testament, and Old Testament (ages 8–11); Faith-in-God: We Love Activity Days and Super Activity Days and Socials (girls 8–11)

- **CURRENT SHARING TIME:** Sharing Fun, Sharing Fun Treasures, and Singing Fun

- **GAMES & ACTIVITIES FOR FAMILY HOME EVENING & PRIMARY** (colored & ready to use): - Activities Series: Gospel Fun Activities, Fun in a Flash, Tons of Fun, Jesus Loves Me - Games Series: Gospel Games and Funner Than Fun Gospel Games - Book with CD Patterns: Short & Sweet with a Treat: 52 Already Done, Ready-for-Fun Family Home Evenings

- **SINGING** (colored & ready to use) Series: Super Little Singers and Super Singing Activities (see Sharing Time, Singing Fun, above)

- **YOUNG WOMEN:** Young Women Fun-tastic! Activities: Lesson Lifesavers for manuals 1–3 and Young Women Fun-tastic! Personal Progress Motivators

Mary Ross, Author

Mary Ross is an energetic mother and has been a Primary teacher and Relief Society president. She loves to help children and Young Women have a good time while learning. She has studied acting, voice, and modeling. Her varied interests include writing, creating activities and children's parties, and cooking. Mary and her husband, Paul, have a daughter, Jennifer. They live in Lehi, Utah.

Jennette Guymon-King, Illustrator

Jennette Guymon-King studied graphic arts and illustration at Utah Valley State College and the University of Utah. She served a mission in Japan. She enjoys sports, reading, cooking, art, gardening, and freelance illustrating. Jennette and her husband, Clayton, live in Bluffdale, Utah. They are the proud parents of daughters Kayla Mae and Shelby, and sons Levi and Carson.

Copyright © 2010 by Mary H. Ross and Jennette Guymon-King - All Rights Reserved
Covenant Communications, Inc., American Fork, Utah, Printed in the United States of America

Sunday Savers™ Activities to Make Learning Fun for Sunbeams—Children Age 3
ISBN-13-978-1-60861-173-7

ACKNOWLEDGMENTS: Thanks to www.creativedelights.com lettering delights for use of fonts for some activities.

INTRODUCTION
Sunday Savers™
Activities to Make Learning Fun
For Sunbeams—Children Age 3

Instant fun has just begun! Family home evening and Primary gospel lessons just got easier with these easy-to-create visuals that will enhance the lessons taught in the *Primary 1* SUNBEAM manual. Parents can use this manual and the visuals here to teach children the gospel of Jesus Christ (as outlined in the manual).

For each lesson, there are two fun activities to choose from. Activity one is easy to cut out and create, and only simple supplies are needed. For the lesson 33 sample shown above, all you'll need is a paper punch and yarn. Activity two is a ready-to-send-off poster with a Home Activity at the bottom (shown left). Parents can use this poster as an opportunity to discuss the lesson concepts taught with their child in family home evening or Sunbeams.

For SUNBEAM children, age 3, we suggest you follow the lesson material that is taught in the *Primary 1* manual. The activities here are not intended to replace the manual concepts—they are merely visuals to help you teach the lessons. More resource material is found on the new Church website: www.new.lds.org. Search the *Quick Links* and *Related Sights* to find Manuals, Scriptures, Magazines, and Music. To find scripture stories, you will need to go through Related Sights–Youth–Quick Links–Children–Scripture Stories.

You will find song suggestions for most lessons and a reference to the *Super Little Singers* book or CD-ROM (shown above/right and on the following page). Here you will find full-color visuals, ready to tear out and use. These visuals will help you teach songs and activities and provide singing motivators.

All the activity handouts in this book can be copied. However, if you want to print them in black and white or color, use the CD-ROM (shown left, sold separately). See the back cover for samples.

DON'T MISS the Sunny Sunday Sack (shown right on p. 153–154). Glue the label and stickers to a bag so children can store activities from this book.

If you are teaching children under age three, use the *Sunday Savers Nursery* book and CD for this age.

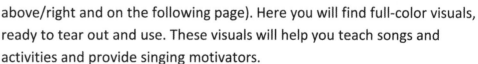

Enjoy More Full-Color, Ready-to-Use Books and CD-ROMs:

With these colored, ready-to-use visuals, you can create memorable learning activities and motivate children to sing and learn in family home evening and Primary. They are also available on CD-ROM so you can print images in color or black-and-white.

Super Singing Activities

You'll find Animal and Insect Do as I'm Doing, Bird in the Leafy Treetops, Build a Prophet, Build a Snowman, Christmas Tree Sing with Me, City of Enoch Meter, Fill Noah's Ark, Follow the Signs, Going Fishing! Keyword Connection, Melody's Family Tree, Name that Tune, Singing Simon, Sunny Sunday Sounds, Temple Flowers "Bee" a Singer, and more.

Super Little Singers

You'll find singing motivators, visuals, and action activities for 28 songs (21 from the Children's Songbook). Enjoy using the visuals for these seven all-time favorite children's songs: Ants Go Marching, Eensy Weensy Spider, Five Little Ducks, Five Little Speckled Frogs, Old MacDonald, Twinkle, Twinkle, Little Star, and Wheels on the Bus.

Table of Contents
Sunday Savers™
Activities to Make Learning Fun—For Sunbeams-Children Age 3

CONTENTS...

LESSON 1   THEME: I Am a Child of God

1. Present lesson on p. 1–3 in the *Primary 1 Sunbeam* manual to help children understand that we are spirit children of Heavenly Father, who knows us and loves us.
2. Present both or one of the following activities to help teach the lesson visually.
3. Sing with children. Sing "I Am a Child of God" and "My Heavenly Father Loves Me" (*Children's Songbook*, 2, 228). For fun visuals, go to the same songs in the *Super Little Singers* book (34, 101) or CD-ROM.
4. Share a thought treat, when appropriate, to match the activity.

Activity 1 – I Am a Child of God – Paper Dolls

1. Copy a set of paper dolls that follows for each boy or girl. Fold flaps down on clothes to hold them on the doll.
2. Talk to children about the dolls, telling them that they are children of God, spirit children of our Heavenly Father.

THOUGHT TREAT: Gingerbread or sugar cookie boy or girl. Roll and cut cookie dough into boy and girl shapes. Bake, frost, and decorate.
Option: Instead of frosting, paint face, hair, and clothes on sugar cookie dough before baking. Paint with a paint brush and cookie paints (mix 2 tsp. can milk with food coloring).

Activity 2 – Child of God Poster

1. Copy the poster that follows for each child to color.
2. Talk about poster, saying, "I am a spirit child of Heavenly Father. He knows me, and He loves me. He sent me to earth to gain a body."
3. Talk about the Home Activity:
• (Part 1) "Ask me how it feels to have a body of flesh and bones." Examples: I'm happy I can walk, talk, breathe, see, hear, taste, and use my body to help.
• (Part 2) "Let's talk about what I can do to keep my body and spirit happy." Examples: (1) BODY. Go to bed and get some sleep. Get up and run and play. Take a bath when it is time. Brush my teeth. Comb my hair. Eat my fruits and vegetables. (2) SPIRIT. Say my prayers each day. Go to Primary and sacrament meeting each week. Have family

home evening. Learn stories in the scriptures. Be kind to others. Help someone. Obey Mother and Father. Help sister and brother.

THOUGHT TREAT: Earth-shaped candy malt balls. Show children earth soil. Explain that we chose to come here to earth. We left our heavenly home, but we can return when it is time.

I am a spirit child of Heavenly Father.

He knows me, and He loves me.
He sent me to earth to gain a body.

Home Activity: Ask me how it feels to have a body of flesh and bones. Let's talk about what I can do to keep my body and spirit happy!

LESSON 2   THEME: Heavenly Father Has a Body

1. Present lesson on p. 7–9 in the *Primary 1 Sunbeam* manual to help children understand that Heavenly Father is a real person with a perfected body of flesh and bones and that we are made in His image.
2. Present both or one of the following activities to help teach the lesson visually.
3. Sing with children. Sing "I Am a Child of God" and "My Heavenly Father Loves Me" (*Children's Songbook*, 2, 228). For fun visuals, go to the same songs in the *Super Little Singers* book (34, 101) or CD-ROM.

Activity 3 – My Body Looks like Heavenly Father and Jesus – Two-sided Puzzle

1. Copy the puzzle that follows for each child. Fold pictures in half and glue back to back, gluing the entire back. Cut into shapes and enclose pieces in an envelope.
2. With Heavenly Father and Jesus on one side, and children on the other side, children can see that we are created in their image.

THOUGHT TREAT: Sugar cookie girl and boy (color clothes with frosting or paint dough with cookie paints before baking). Cookie Paints: Mix 2 tsp canned milk with 2–3 drops food coloring.

Activity 4 – Created in God's Image Poster

1. Copy the poster that follows for each child to color.
2. Talk about poster, saying, "Heavenly Father is a real person. I am made in His image. He has a perfect body of flesh and bones. I can become like Him."
• Image Spotlight. Ahead of time, learn good things about children to tell the class, building up their self-image.
• Cheer (with optional pom-poms from dollar store). "Two, four, six, eight. Who do I appreciate? Me, me! Heavenly Father created me, terrific me!" Mention at least one thing that is terrific about each child.
3. Talk about the Home Activity: "Look into the mirror with me and tell me the color of my eyes. Tell me about my face, ears, hair, hands, and feet. Tell me how wonderful I am."

THOUGHT TREAT: Straight-and-strong pretzels. Give children straight pretzels and tell them that their body is straight and strong. Talk about things that will help them keep their body straight and strong.

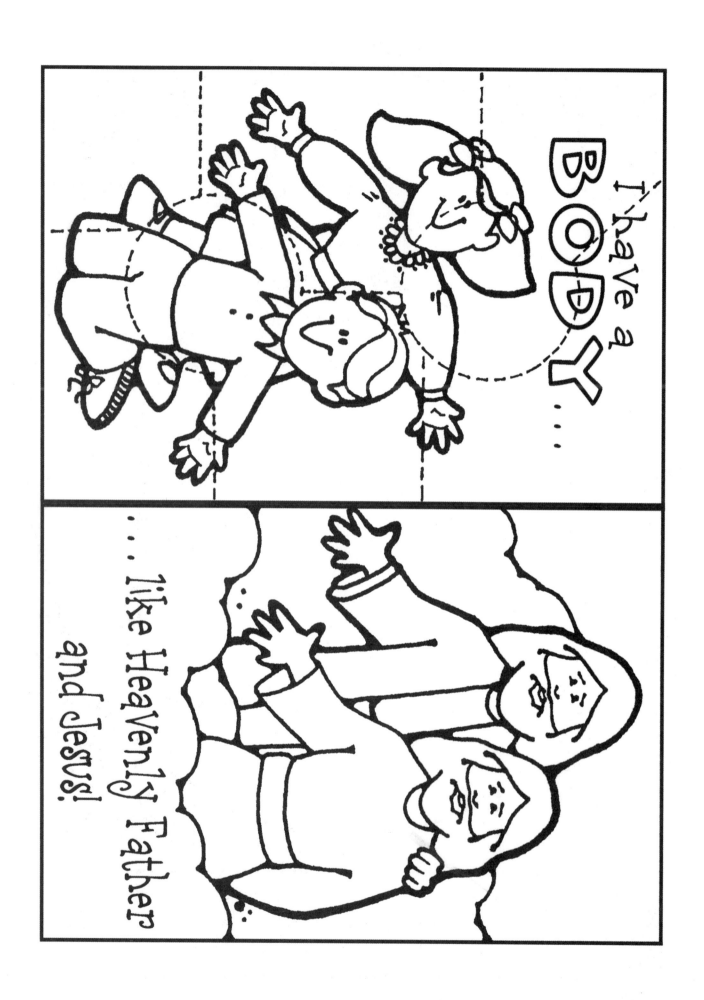

I am made in His image.

Heavenly Father is a real person.

He has a perfect body of flesh and bones.

I can become like Him.

Home Activity: Look into the mirror with me and tell me the color of my eyes. Tell me about my face, ears, hair, hands, and feet. Tell me how wonderful I am.

LESSON 3   THEME: Heavenly Father's Plan for Us

1. Present lesson on p. 7–9 in the *Primary 1 Sunbeam* manual to help children understand that we lived with Heavenly Father as spirit children before we came to earth and that we can live with Him again after this life.

2. Present both or one of the following activities to help teach the lesson visually.

3. Sing with children. Sing "I Am a Child of God" and "My Heavenly Father Loves me" *Children's Songbook*, 2, 228). For fun visuals, go to the same songs in the *Super Little Singers* book (34, 101) or CD-ROM.

Activity 5 - Paper Dolls with Heavenly & Earthly Home

1. Copy the paper doll with heavenly and earthly home that follows for each child. Mount homes on a sheet of paper, cutting a slit where shown before mounting on edges only. Cut dolls out with head on fold line of a sheet of plastic (to make spirit doll).

2. Use the plastic spirit body. Start by sliding body into the heaven premortal life slot, then slide it into the earth slot, joining spirit with body. Last, slide it into heaven after death, and join again with body to show resurrection state.

THOUGHT TREAT: (1) Heaven and earth cookie. Frost cookie with white clouds on top and chocolate earth on bottom. (2) Heaven and Earth Pudding Art. Form a cloud and earth with vanilla and chocolate pudding on waxed paper. Eat the pudding picture.

Activity 6 – Happiness Plan Poster

1. Copy the poster that follows for each child to color.

2. Talk about poster, saying, "Heavenly Father has a plan of happiness for me! When we were living in heaven as spirits, Heavenly Father presented His plan for us. Part of the plan was to come to earth to receive physical bodies to be like Him and be able to return to His presence. Through Jesus's Atonement and our obedience, we can return. In heaven we were with Heavenly Father and Jesus. We chose to follow Jesus. With this body, we can learn to make right choices so we can return to live with Heavenly Father and Jesus someday."

3. Talk about the Home Activity: "Show me a glove to illustrate the body (lifeless without the spirit). When I came to earth, my spirit was placed in my body to bring it to life (put hand in glove). When I die, my spirit will leave my body (remove hand from glove). When I am resurrected, my spirit will return to my body (put glove back on)."

THOUGHT TREAT: Heavenly smile bread. Squirt a processed cheese smile on a slice of bread for each child. Remind children that heaven is a happy place because Heavenly Father and Jesus are there. They want us to be happy while we live on the earth too.

I am Heavenly Father's spirit child.

I came to earth for a body.

Heavenly Father has a Plan for me!

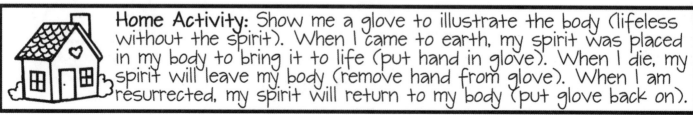

Home Activity: Show me a glove to illustrate the body (lifeless without the spirit). When I came to earth, my spirit was placed in my body to bring it to life (put hand in glove). When I die, my spirit will leave my body (remove hand from glove). When I am resurrected, my spirit will return to my body (put glove back on).

LESSON 4   THEME: I Can Pray to Heavenly Father

1. Present lesson on p. 10–12 in the *Primary 1 Sunbeam* manual to help children learn how to pray to Heavenly Father and know that He will listen to their prayers.
2. Present both or one of the following activities to help teach the lesson visually.
3. Sing with children. Sing "I Am Like a Star" (*Children's Songbook*, 163). For fun visuals, go to the same song in the *Super Little Singers* book (61) or CD-ROM.

Activity 7 – I Can Pray to Heavenly Father – Daniel and Lions' Den Drama Scene

1. Copy and cut out the drama scene that follows for each child.
2. Use the props and figures to act out the Daniel and Lions' Den story where Daniel prayed to Heavenly Father. Then the lions did not eat Daniel (Daniel 6).

THOUGHT TREAT: Cream-filled cookies or crackers. Say, "These cookies or crackers are like our hands in prayer. They come together and are folded and quiet. Then when the prayer is over, they can unfold (take cookie apart). After the prayer is over, let's remember to keep our hands still. Keep your hands folded or in your lap in Primary. This is being reverent in Heavenly Father's house."

Activity 8 – Prayer Poster

1. Copy the poster that follows for each child to color.
2. Talk about poster as you help children learn to pray. Tell them to: (1) Open their prayer with, "Dear Heavenly Father." (2) Thank Heavenly Father for their many blessings. (3) Ask Heavenly Father for the things they need. (4) Close their prayer by saying, "in the name of Jesus Christ, amen." Show this poster and review each week to help children learn to pray.
3. Talk about the Home Activity:
• (Part 1) "Help me remember to say my own prayers in the morning and at night." Talk about kneeling beside your bed to pray when you get up in the morning and before you get into bed at night.
• (Part 2) "Remind me that Heavenly Father will listen whenever I need to talk." Tell them about different situations at home and away, explaining that they can talk to Heavenly Father in prayer anywhere and at any time, day or night. Look them in the eyes and say, "He sees you," and hold up your hands to your ears and say, "He hears you too."

THOUGHT TREAT: Reverent eyes cookies. Tell children that when we pray to Heavenly Father, we should fold our arms and close our eyes. Doing this helps us think of what to pray for and to listen. Show them the cookie and say, "Think of this cookie as our eyes when we pray. We open them to see things and we close them to pray" (open and close cookie).

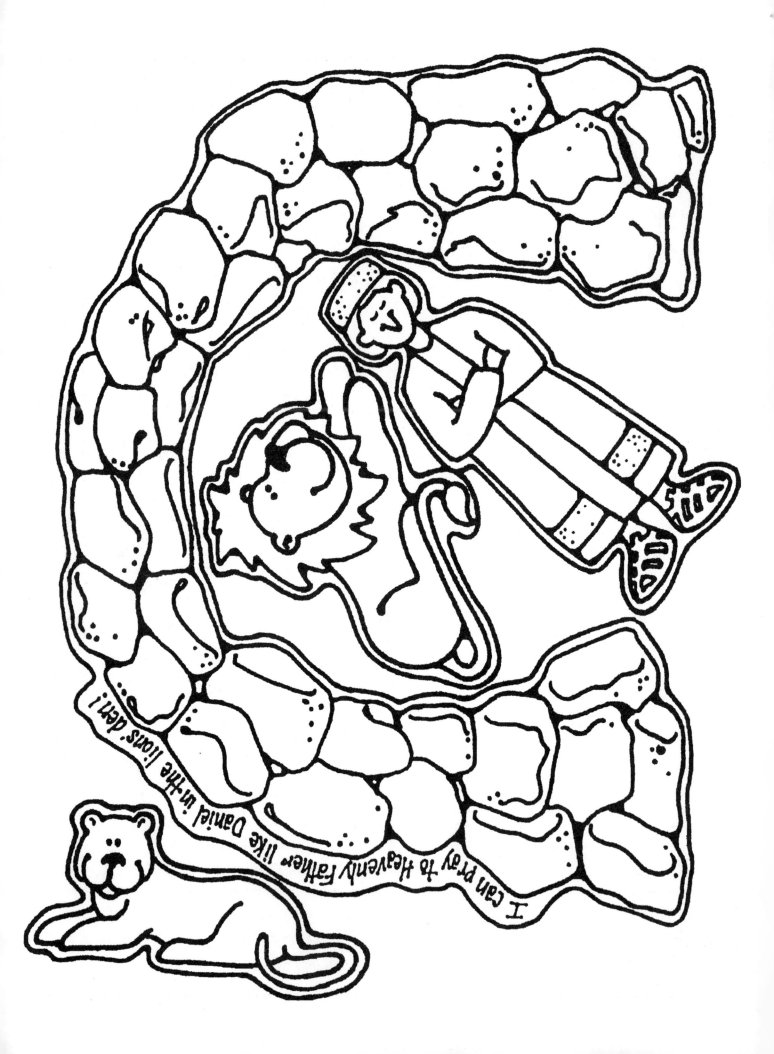

I can pray to Heavenly Father like Daniel in the lions' den!

1 To open your prayer say, "Dear Heavenly Father."

2 Thank Heavenly Father for your many blessings.

3 Ask Heavenly Father for the things you need.

4 To close your prayer say, "in the name of Jesus Christ, amen."

Home Activity: Help me to remember to say my own prayers in the morning and at night. Remind me that Heavenly Father will listen whenever I need to talk.

LESSON 5   THEME: Jesus Christ Is the Son of Heavenly Father

1. Present lesson on p. 13–14 in the *Primary 1 Sunbeam* manual to help each child understand that Jesus Christ is Heavenly Father's son.
2. Present both or one of the following activities to help teach the lesson visually.
3. Sing with children. Sing "I Am a Child of God" and "Away in a Manger" (*Children's Songbook*, 2, 42). For fun actions, go to the same song in the *Super Little Singers* book (34, 157) or CD-ROM.

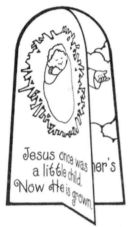

Activity 9 – Jesus is Heavenly Father's Son – 3-D Stand-up Card

1. Copy the card that follows for each child. Before cutting out, fan-fold card in five places (dotted lines specify fold location). Glue sides A, B, and C together to make a three-sided card.
2. This three-sided stand-up card shows that Jesus is Heavenly Father's Son and that Jesus obeys Heavenly Father. Tell children that when we do what is right, we are obeying Jesus and Heavenly Father. Children can say, "Jesus once was a little child like me. He learned to obey Heavenly Father and so can I."

THOUGHT TREAT: Sunshine lollipop cookie. Make cake mix recipe below; frost cookies white. Then, using a cake decorator tube filled with yellow frosting, make a sun. Lollipop cookie recipe: One 18–ounce yellow cake mix, 3/4 cup water, and 2 eggs--Drop by tablespoons full, three inches apart, onto cookie sheet. Place wooden craft sticks into dough. Bake 8–11 minutes at 375°. NOTE: Remind children that the sun is a special light Heavenly Father gave us to keep us warm and give us light. Jesus is also a special light. He is Heavenly Father's Son. He came to earth to help us choose the right.

Activity 10 – Jesus and Heavenly Father Poster

1. Copy the poster that follows for each child to color.
2. Talk about poster, saying, "Jesus Christ is Heavenly Father's Son."Jesus loves Heavenly Father and obeys Him just like we obey our parents. We love Jesus and Heavenly Father.
• Say, "As a baby, Jesus was born to an earthly mother, Mary, yet He was Heavenly Father's real Son. In the manger where He lay, you could find a cow, donkey, and sheep. Shepherds came to see Him, and wise men brought Him gifts. Many had waited a long time for Jesus to come."
• Say, "As a 12-year-old boy, Jesus was found teaching the wise men in the temple. They listened to the stories of Jesus. We can listen as our parents and teachers tell us the stories of Jesus. We can be kind to others and help those in need like Jesus did."
3. Talk about the Home Activity: "Tell me the stories about when Jesus was a little baby and what He did when He was a young boy. Show me how to be like Jesus."

THOUGHT TREAT: Follow-that-star cookie. Make sugar cookie dough and cut into star shapes, then bake and frost. Tell children that a new star shown bright over the manger that special night to tell the shepherds and wise men where to find the baby Jesus.

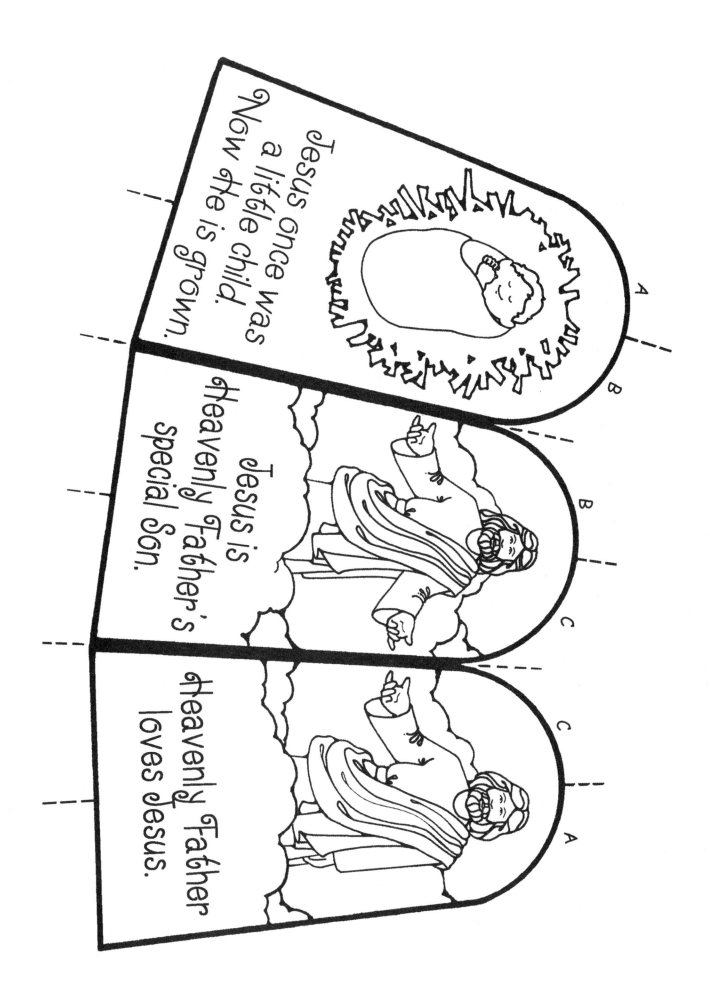

Jesus once was
a little child.
Now He is grown.

Jesus is
Heavenly Father's
special Son.

Heavenly Father
loves Jesus.

A   B   C   A   B   C

Jesus Christ is Heavenly Father's Son.

Home Activity: Tell me stories about when Jesus was a little baby and what He did when He was a young boy. Show me how to be like Jesus.

LESSON 6   THEME: Heavenly Father and Jesus Love Me

1. Present lesson on p. 15–18 in the *Primary 1 Sunbeam* manual to help children feel that Heavenly Father and Jesus Christ love each of us and that His love will never change.

2. Present both or one of the following activities to help teach the lesson visually.

3. Sing with children. Sing "Jesus Loved the Little Children" and "My Heavenly Father Loves Me" (*Children's Songbook*, 59, 228). For fun visuals, go to the same songs in the *Super Little Singers* book (61, 101) or CD-ROM.

Activity 11 – Heavenly Father and Jesus Love Me – Hearts-On-A-String

1. Copy hearts that follow for each child. Punch holes in hearts and tie together with string, tying a knot between each heart to keep apart (optional).

2. Hearts remind children that Heavenly Father and Jesus love them.

3. Sing "My Heavenly Father Loves Me" (see #3 above). Allow children to look at images as you sing the song. After singing, point to the child's chest and say, "Your heart is in here."

THOUGHT TREAT: Heart-shaped cookies or candies. Tell children that Heavenly Father and His Son, Jesus, love us. They gave us this beautiful world so we can be happy. Let's tell Them we love Them when we pray, and thank Heavenly Father for (name items from hearts on-a-string): birds, sky, rain, wind, rose, lilac tree, eyes, ears, body, and butterfly.

Activity 12 – Love Photo Poster

1. Copy the poster that follows for each child to color. Glue a photo of child in the bottom heart. You will need to take a photo of each child a week before. If this is not possible, draw the child's face in the heart instead.

2. Talk about poster, saying, "Heavenly Father Loves Me, Jesus Loves Me, and I Love Heavenly Father and Jesus."

3. Talk about the Home Activity: "Hold a mirror up to me and tell me that Heavenly Father and Jesus love me very much."

THOUGHT TREAT: Blessings basket. Have children take food from a basket to share (e.g, cheese [from a cow], orange [from a tree], crackers [from wheat]).Talk about each item by saying, "Heavenly Father and Jesus gave us (item) because They love us." Say a blessing on the food before eating.

Heavenly Father Loves Me

Jesus Loves Me

← Draw a picture of you in the circle.

I Love Heavenly Father and Jesus

 **Home Activity:** Hold a mirror up to me and tell me that Heavenly Father and Jesus love me very much.

LESSON 7   THEME: The Holy Ghost Helps Me

1. Present lesson on p. 19–21 in the *Primary 1 Sunbeam* manual to help children understand that the Holy Ghost helps us with many things.
2. Present both or one of the following activities to help teach the lesson visually.
3. Sing with children. Sing "I Am a Child of God" and "I Am Like a Star" (*Children's Songbook*, 2, 163).
For fun visuals, go to the same songs in the *Super Little Singers* book (34, 61) or CD-ROM.

Activity 13 – The Gift of the Holy Ghost – Gift Package

1. Copy the gift package that follows for each child. Cut a soft piece of fabric to enclose. Cut a slit on the line to insert the heart, Holy Ghost, and soft fabric as you tell them He is the Comforter.
2. This Holy Ghost gift package shows children that the Holy Ghost is a special gift we can receive after we are baptized.
3. Explain that the Holy Ghost does not have a body, so he can be Heavenly Father's and Jesus's helper. He can whisper the truth in our hearts and minds. He can help us make right choices. He can warn us if danger is near. He can give us a feeling of peace when we are sad. He is our Comforter (show soft piece of fabric).

THOUGHT TREAT: Heart-shaped cookie.

Activity 14 – Holy Ghost Helper Poster

1. Copy the poster that follows for each child to color.
2. Talk about poster, saying, "The Holy Ghost can speak to our heart and to our mind. The Holy Ghost can bring us comfort and light. The Holy Ghost helps us know what is right."
• Bring a blanket/comforter that children can hold and cuddle up with. Talk about how nice it is to feel safe and warm with this blanket around them. Tell them that the Holy Ghost is the Comforter who helps our mind and spirit feel safe and warm.
• Bring a flashlight or lamp. Tell children that when it is dark we turn on the light so we can see where we are and what we are doing. The light helps us feel safe. The Holy Ghost is a light that helps our mind and our spirit see right choices so we can choose the right and be happy.
3. Talk about the Home Activity: "Help me pray for the Holy Ghost to guide me. Help me know when He is helping me."

THOUGHT TREAT: Sweet-spirit straws. Give each child a straw to blow from. Talk about the special spirit of the Holy Ghost. Blow from the straw onto their hands and say, "The Holy Ghost does not have a body. We can't see Him, but we can feel Him. We know He is near because good ideas come to our mind, and we have a warm feeling in our heart when something is right."

The Holy Ghost has a spirit body.

The Holy Ghost can dwell in my heart. ♡

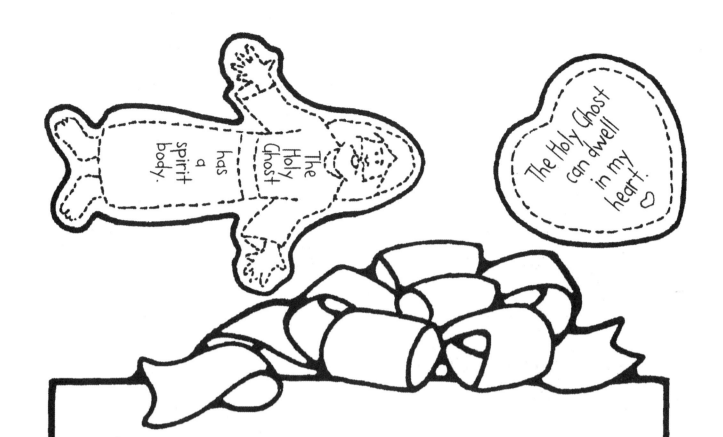

The Gift of the

HOLY GHOST

Fold   Fold

The Holy Ghost will:
1. Help me know what is right.
2. Help me know that Jesus and Heavenly Father are real.
3. Give me comfort and help.

The Holy Ghost can speak to our heart and our mind.

The Holy Ghost helps us to know what is right.

right

The Holy Ghost can bring us comfort and light.

The Holy Ghost will help me.

Home Activity: Help me pray for the Holy Ghost to guide me. Help me to know when He is helping me.

LESSON 8   THEME: I Am Thankful for the Day and Night

1. Present lesson on p. 22–23 in the *Primary 1 Sunbeam* manual to help each child understand that following Heavenly Father's plan, Jesus Christ created the day so we can work and play and the night so we can rest.

2. Present both or one of the following activities to help teach the lesson visually.

3. Sing with children. Sing "I Am Like a Star" (*Children's Songbook*, 163) and "Twinkle, Twinkle, Little Star." For fun visuals go to the same songs in the *Super Little Singers* book (61, 131) or CD ROM. You can find the words and lyrics for "Twinkle, Twinkle, Little Star" in the *Super Little Singers* book (100) or CD-ROM. Sing "Saturday" (*Children's Songbook*, 196). For fun action ideas, go to the same song in the *Super Little Singers* book (160) or CD-ROM.

Activity 15 – Day and Night I Give Thanks - Window Wheel

1. Copy the window wheel parts A and B that follow. Attach parts by piercing a paper fastener in the center so the wheel turns.

2. Talk about this day and night window wheel and about how Heavenly Father divided the day and the night for us to work, play, and rest.

THOUGHT TREAT: Cut-out cookies in sun, moon, and star shapes.

Activity 16 – Night and Day Poster

1. Copy the poster that follows for each child to color.

2. Talk about poster, saying, "I am thankful for each night and day!"

• Tell children that Heavenly Father had a plan to help us, so Jesus created the earth, sun, moon, and stars— the earth to live on, the sun to keep us warm and light the day, and the moon and stars to light the night.

• Recite action poem, "Sun in the day, lights my way for work and play." (Put arms above head in circle.) "Moon and stars at night, help me sleep tight." (Put hands together under chin and close eyes.)

3. Talk about the Home Activity: "Help me learn to work so I can be like Heavenly Father and Jesus. Help me play so I can be happy. Help me pray at night before I go to bed so I will feel safe and go to sleep."

THOUGHT TREAT: Sun, moon, and star cookies. Cut out cookies in these shapes and sprinkle with colored sugar before baking. Talk about each celestial body and what it represents (night and day). Ask children what they can do to show they are thankful for each.

Push brad
through center
mark (*).

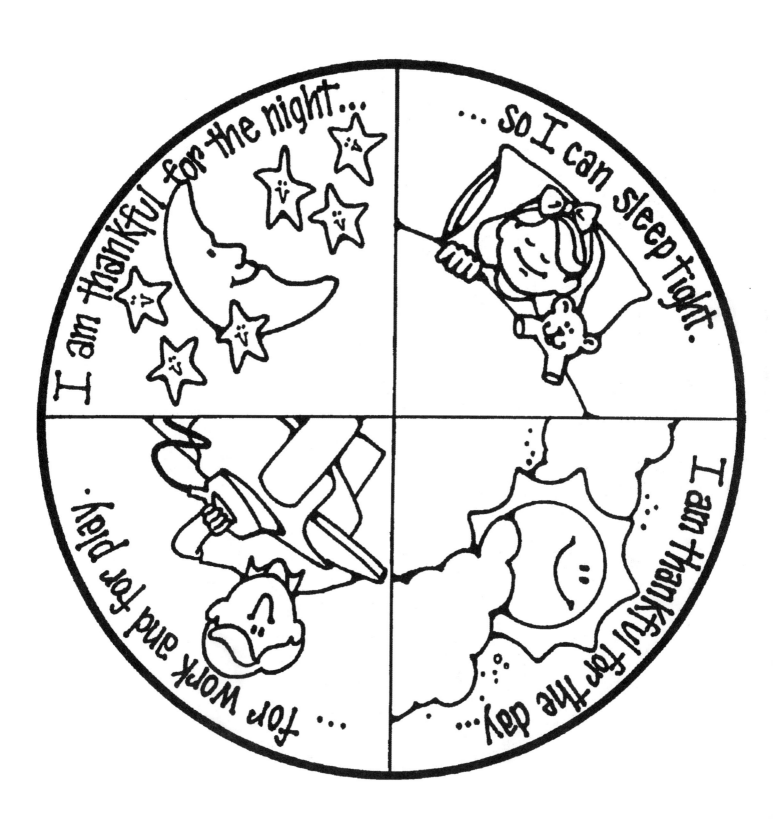

I am thankful for each night and day!

 **Home Activity:** Help me learn to work so I can be like Heavenly Father and Jesus. Help me play so I can be happy. Help me pray at night before I go to bed so I will feel safe and go to sleep.

LESSON 9   THEME: I Am Thankful for Water

1. Present lesson on p. 25–27 in the *Primary 1 Sunbeam* manual to help children feel gratitude to Heavenly Father and Jesus Christ for water.
2. Present both or one of the following activities to help teach the lesson visually.
3. Sing with children. Sing "Baptism," (*Children's Songbook*, 100).

Activity 17 – I Can Be Baptized In Water like Jesus – Baptism Water Wheel

I can be baptized in the water like Jesus.

1. Copy the water wheel parts A and B that follow for each child. Attach wheel to sun frame with a paper fastener. Glue water to sun frame where indicated.
2. Baptism water wheel shows children how they can be baptized in the water (by immersion) like Jesus. Turn the wheel to show how figures go under the water to be baptized. Tell children that at age eight they can be baptized in the water like Jesus.
3. See "Water Is Important in the Church" on page 26 in lesson 9 of the *Primary 1* manual and talk about Jesus's baptism and how water is used in the sacrament.

THOUGHT TREAT: Water cookie. Frost a sugar cookie with blue frosting to look like water. Give them water to drink and talk about how water is used for many things.

Activity 18 – Jesus Created Water Poster

Home Activity: During the week, help me be thankful that Jesus created water.

1. Copy the poster that follows for each child to color. Activity helps children feel gratitude for water. They can thank Heavenly Father and Jesus for water. See *Emphasis on Baptism and Sacrament* (below).
2. Talk about poster, saying, "I love water!"
• Help children answer questions:
—"What do you think would happen if you took a bath in tomato soup instead?" (You can show some tomato soup.)
—"Can you find the animal that lives in water?" (Help them find the fish.)
—"Do you know what ice is made of?" (Put ice cubes in each child's drink.)
• Talk about uses for water: I am thankful for water that comes from the sky, filling our lakes, rivers, and oceans. I use water for many things. I drink it, bathe in it, and use it to wash my hair and clothes. I use it to wash dishes, water the flowers and other plants, and water my pets.
• *Emphasis on Baptism and Sacrament:* I can be baptized in water like Jesus when I am eight. When we partake of the sacrament water each week, we remember Jesus.
3. Talk about the Home Activity: "During the week, help me be thankful that Jesus created water."

THOUGHT TREAT: Water. You can add ice cubes or blue food coloring, talking about how the blue sky reflects on the water (but the water is not blue—just a reflection).

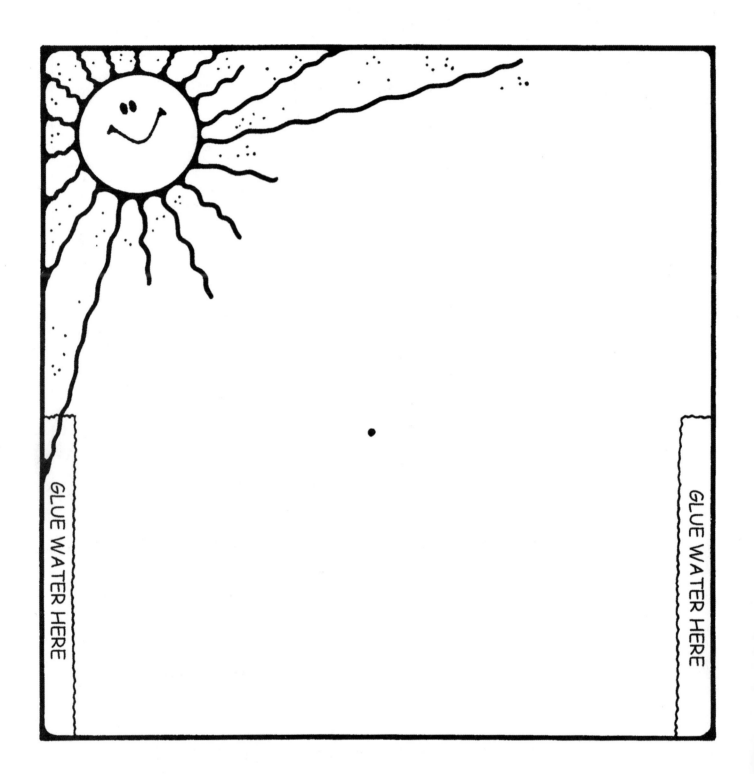

GLUE WATER HERE

GLUE WATER HERE

I can be baptized
in the water like Jesus.

Home Activity: During the week, help me be thankful that Jesus created water.

LESSON 10   THEME: I am thankful for Trees, Plants, and Flowers

1. Present lesson on p. 28–30 in the *Primary 1 Sunbeam* manual to help children feel gratitude to Heavenly Father and Jesus Christ for trees, plants, and flowers. When we pray, we can thank Them for these beautiful creations that help us.

2. Present both or one of the following activities to help teach the lesson visually.

3. Sing with children. Sing "In the Leafy Treetops" and "Popcorn Popping" (*Children's Songbook*, 240, 242). For fun activities, go to the same songs in the *Super Little Singers* book (159, 160) or CD-ROM.

Activity 19 – Heaven-sent Garden – Bracelets or Binoculars

Copy the garden images that follow for each child. Fold and glue or tape into triangle shapes to use as follows:

Bracelets: Children love to use these as bracelets, slipping them over their hands.

Binoculars: Children like to look through them, pretending they are binoculars and looking up and down and all around the room. They look at nature, the teacher, and the other children through these fun triangular shapes.

THOUGHT TREAT: Edible plants: apples, carrots, celery, or broccoli. Children like to call broccoli "trees."

Activity 20 – I Love Nature Poster

1. Copy the poster that follows for each child to color.

2. Talk about poster, saying, "I love the plants, flowers, and trees. They bless our lives, both you and me."

• Ask children to: (1) think of another fruit that grows on a tree; (2) name animals and birds that live in trees (e.g., squirrel, monkey, chipmunk, leopard, snake, owl, or robin); (3) name your favorite vegetable; (4) name your favorite flower; (5) list what you would like to plant in a garden; (6) tell what you like most about trees (e.g., they are homes for animals, we can climb them, we can pick fruit from them, we can sit in their shade).

• Growing plant actions: Make up actions to go with trees, plants, and flowers as you sing to the tune of "Once There Was a Snowman," (*Children's Songbook*, 249). Sing, "I can plant a tree, tree, tree . . . water it and watch it grow . . . tall, tall, tall."

3. Talk about the Home Activity: "Take me for a walk to look at the trees, plants, and flowers and help me pray to thank Heavenly Father for these creations."

THOUGHT TREAT: Apple and seeds. Cut up apple slices and serve with sunflower seeds.

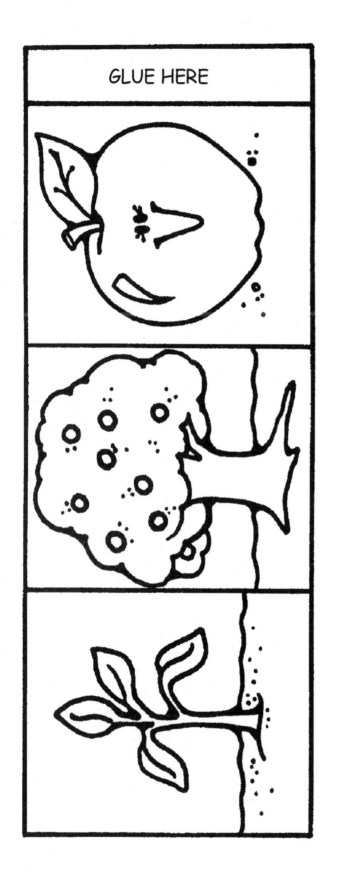
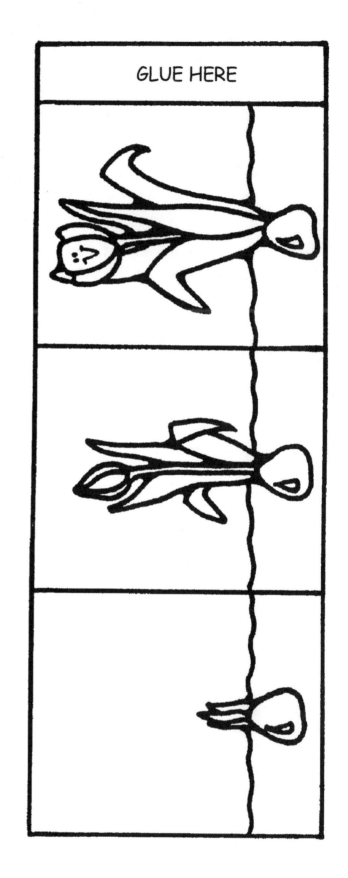

I love the plants, flowers, and trees.
They bless our lives, both you and me!

Can you think of another fruit that grows on a tree?

Can you name an animal that lives in a tree?

What do you like most about trees?

If you had a garden, what would you plant in it?

What is your favorite vegetable?

What color is your favorite flower?

Home Activity: Take me for a walk to look at the trees, plants, and flowers and help me pray to thank Heavenly Father for these creations.

LESSON II THEME: I Am Thankful for Fish

1. Present lesson on p. 31–34 in the *Primary 1 Sunbeam* manual to help each child feel gratitude to Heavenly Father and Jesus Christ for fish and water animals.
2. Present both or one of the following activities to help teach the lesson visually.
3. Sing with children. Sing "Five Little Speckled Frogs." For fun visuals, words, and music, go to the same song in the *Super Little Singers* book (33, 198) or CD-ROM. See the "Go Fishing! Choose a Song" motivator visuals in the *Super Little Singers* book (163) or CD-ROM.

Activity 21 – Jonah and the Whale – Slide-show

1. Copy the Jonah scene that follows for each child. Cut along dashed lines in whale's mouth and water, inserting the pull-through picture strip into slits on the side and in the whale's mouth. Fold back edges of picture strip to prevent pulling all the way out.
2. Tell the story of Jonah and the BIG whale-size fish that swallowed Jonah (Jonah 1–3). Talk about why we are thankful for fish and how Jonah was saved from drowning when the fish swallowed him. God wanted Jonah to be safe, so He allowed the fish to swallow Jonah until he repented and said he would be a prophet to tell the people to repent.

THOUGHT TREAT: *Idea 1:* Squishy fishy. Create fish-shaped gelatin. Make the firm gelatin jigglers recipe. Spray pie tins with cooking spray, pour gelatin dessert into pie tins to set up (refrigerate 2–4 hours). Lay firm gelatin onto waxed paper and cut out fish shapes with a knife. Children love the squishy fishy feel as this dessert slithers in their mouths. *Idea 2:* Fishy snacks. Candy gummy fish or fish-shaped crackers in a fish bowl or bag.

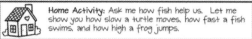

Home Activity: Ask me how fish help us. Let me show you how slow a turtle moves, how fast a fish swims, and how high a frog jumps.

Activity 22 – Fish Thanks Poster

1. Copy the poster that follows for each child to color.
2. Talk about poster, saying, "I am thankful for fish!" and other animals that live in water, like frogs, turtles, whales, crabs, and seals. A prophet named Jonah was swallowed by a big fish and lived inside it for three days. He told Heavenly Father he would preach repentance to the people as He had commanded. Then the fish spit him out on dry land.
3. Talk about the Home Activity: "Ask me how fish help us. Let me show you how slow a turtle moves, how fast a fish swims, and how high a frog jumps."

THOUGHT TREAT: Fish-shaped crackers. Children can fish these out of a fish bowl. Or they can fish over a mock clothesline (sheet draped over a rope) to catch a bag of fish crackers. Tie a string to a wooden dowel and attach a paper clip they can toss over clothesline. Attach the bag of crackers to the paperclip. Tell children that fish always live in water because they can only breathe under water (but we can't).

How many turtles can you count?

Can you find the fish that are praying?

Can you color the frog green?

Can you find a fish with a tiny baby fish?

I Am Thankful for Fish!

Home Activity: Ask me how fish help us. Let me show you how slow a turtle moves, how fast a fish swims, and how high a frog jumps.

LESSON 12   THEME: I Am Thankful for Animals

1. Present lesson on p. 35–37 in the *Primary 1 Sunbeam* manual to help children feel gratitude toward Heavenly Father and Jesus Christ for animals.
2. Present both or one of the following activities to help teach the lesson visually.
3. Sing with children. Sing "Old McDonald." For fun visuals, go to song in the *Super Little Singers* book (101) or CD-ROM.

Activity 23 – Animals Saved From the Flood – Noah's 3-D Ark

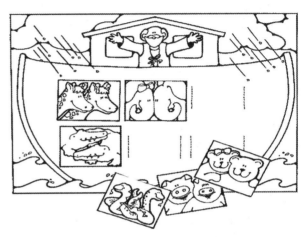

1. Copy the ark scene that follows for each child. Cut out slits in the ark and insert animal tabs into slits. Animals will bend in "U" shape to produce a 3–D effect.
2. This 3-D Noah's Ark will help children save animals from the flood by placing animals in slots.

THOUGHT TREAT: Animal-shaped cookies or crackers.

Activity 24 – Animals All Over the World! Poster

1. Copy the poster that follows for each child to color.
2. <u>Talk about poster</u>, saying, "Animals all over the world!" Help children answer the questions:
—"If you had a giraffe for a pet, where would he sleep?"
—"If you could move like a monkey, what would you like to climb?"
—"If you could see like an owl at night, would you be afraid of the dark?"
• Help children make animal sounds of animals on the handout (e.g., monkey) (see "Thought Treat" below), meow, moo, woof, caw, who-who, quack. Say what each animal does to help us.
3. <u>Talk about the Home Activity</u>: "Look at a book of animals with me and help me discover how many different animals were created for our wondrous world!"

THOUGHT TREAT: Monkey food. Give each child a banana and have him or her peel it like monkeys do (as shown in handout above). Before taking each bite, children can make monkey sounds, "Oo-oo-ee-ee-aa-aa." After they eat the banana, have children scratch under their arms like a monkey and pretend to jump from tree limb to limb.

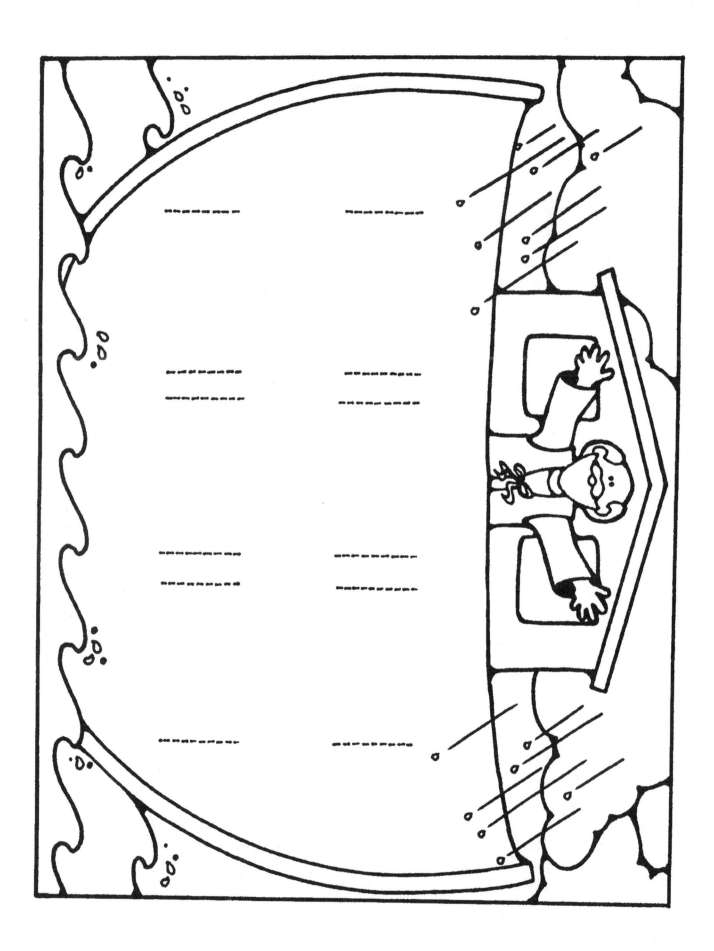

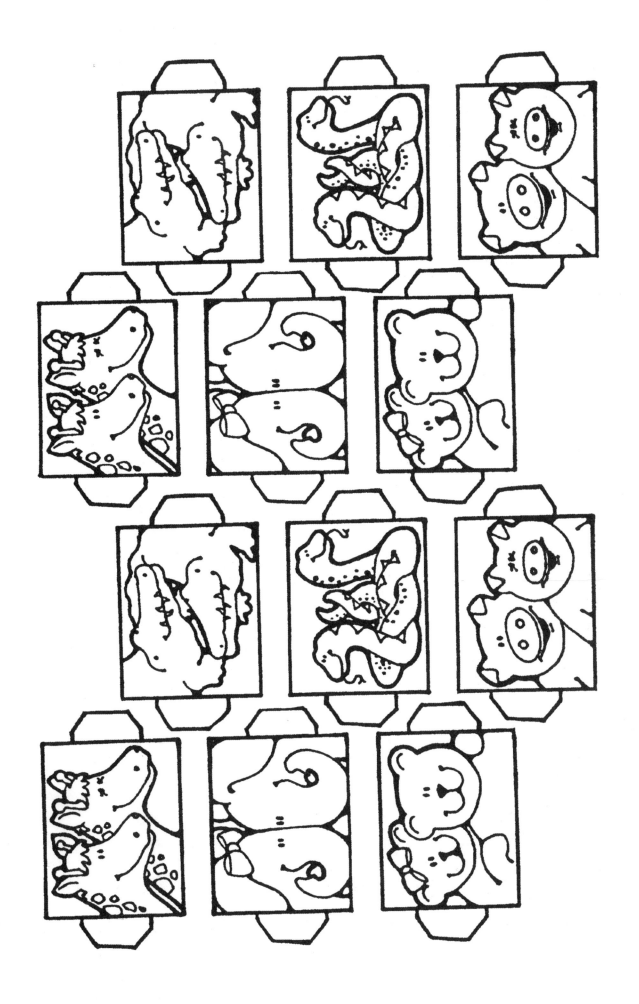

Animals All Over the World!

If you had a giraffe for a pet, where would he sleep? If you could move like a monkey, what would you like to climb? If you could see like an owl at night, would you be afraid of the dark?

Home Activity: Look at a book of animals with me and help me discover how many different animals were created for our wondrous world!

LESSON 13   THEME: *I Am Thankful for Birds and Insects*

1. Present lesson on p. 38–41 in the *Primary 1 Sunbeam* manual to help children feel gratitude to Heavenly Father and Jesus Christ for birds, insects, and creeping things.

2. Present both or one of the following activities to help teach the lesson visually.

3. Sing with children. Sing "In the Leafy Treetops" (*Children's Songbook*, 240) and "Five Little Ducks." For fun actions, visuals, and motivators, go to the same songs in the *Super Little Singers* book (159, 33, 167, 197) or CD-ROM. Sing "Ants Go Marching," "Eensy Weensy Spider," and "Five Little Speckled Frogs." For fun visuals, music, and lyrics, go to the same songs in the *Super Little Singers* book (1-2, 22, 195-196, 198) or CD-ROM.

Activity 25 – Birds, Insects, & Creeping Things
- Caterpillar/Cocoon/Butterfly Pull-up & Finger Puppet

1. Copy the butterfly puppet images that follow for each child. Cut slits in butterfly finger puppet and top and bottom pockets of cocoon. Glue outside edge of cocoon 1/4", gluing back to back. Punch a hole at the top and thread a string through the hole to hang. Slide caterpillar and butterfly in and out (folding butterfly to fit).

2. Images help children put on a puppet show where the caterpillar goes into cocoon and a butterfly comes out—the caterpillar becomes a real butterfly.

3. Tell The Butterfly Story: *A butterfly begins as a tiny egg that hatches into a caterpillar. The caterpillar eats and grows. It sheds its skin several times as the caterpillar grows to full size. Then it forms a protective shell called a cocoon. When it breaks, its shell opens out into a butterfly.*

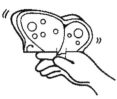

4. Place a butterfly on the child's finger, sliding finger through slits. Child can wiggle finger and watch butterfly fly.

THOUGHT TREAT: Butterfly cookies. Cut out sugar cookies in butterfly shapes and frost. You can paint cookies with cookie paints (2 Tb can milk to 2 drops food coloring) before baking. No messy frosting needed. Sing the following to the tune of Old McDonald. "Butterflies just flutter by, in the flower patch. Caterpillars they once were, from cocoons they hatch. With a flutter here and a flutter there, here they fly, there they fly, right in front of my two eyes. Butterflies just flutter by, in the flower patch."

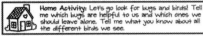

Activity 26 – Birds and Insects Poster

1. Copy the poster that follows for each child to color.

2. Talk about poster, saying, "Birds and bugs deserve our hugs! We thank you!"

• Talk about how hugs for birds and bugs are different from hugs for our family and friends. To hug a bird or a bug, you don't squeeze them like you do Mom or Dad. Hugging a bird or bug will hurt them because they are so small. "Hugging" a bird or bug is watching out for them and helping them find their home. A bird's home might be in a tree, and a bug's home might be in the dirt near a rock they can crawl under. (But don't put the rock on top of them, because it might squish them.)

• Help children answer questions found on the handout (e.g., "Spiders catch insects—like mosquitos—in their webs! How many spiders can you find?"). Then find the ladybugs, worms, and caterpillars.

3. Talk about the Home Activity: "Let's go look for bugs and birds! Tell me which bugs are helpful to us and which ones we should leave alone. Tell me what you know about all the different birds we see."

THOUGHT TREAT: Pretzel bird nests. Pile stick pretzels in a bowl to look like a bird nest.

I'm thankful for the beautiful BUTTERFLIES!

Birds and bugs deserve our hugs! We thank you!

Spiders catch insects (like mosquitos) in their webs! How many can you find?

How many can you find? How many can you find? Caterpillars or worms (like silk worms) can help us. How many can you find?

Ladybugs eat hundreds of aphids that harm fruit trees and roses! How many can you find?

Home Activity: Let's go look for bugs and birds! Tell me which bugs are helpful to us and which ones we should leave alone. Tell me what you know about all the different birds we see.

LESSON 14   THEME: Adam & Eve Were Created in Heavenly Father's Image

1. Present lesson on p. 42–44 in the *Primary 1 Sunbeam* manual to help children understand that Adam and Eve were created in the image of Heavenly Father, just like we are.

2. Present both or one of the following activities to help teach the lesson visually.

3. Sing with children. Sing "I Am a Child of God" (*Children's Songbook*, 2). For fun visuals, go to the same song in the *Super Little Singers* book (34) or CD-ROM. Sing "Head, Shoulders, Knees, and Toes" and "Hinges" (*Children's Songbook*, 275, 277). For fun action activities, go to the same song in the *Super Little Singers* book (158) or CD-ROM.

Activity 27 – Adam and Eve's Image – Paper Doll Pleats

1. Copy the paper doll pattern and Adam and Eve poster that follows for each child. With poster base ready to mount dolls on, do the following: (1) Measure 1 1/2" on edge of an 8 ½" x 11" paper and fan-fold paper lengthwise into six folds. Cut out and trace paper doll pattern on top fold and cut out shape to find three connecting images. Glue paper doll pleats in place below poster sign. Draw in faces and hair, and color.

2. Images show that Adam and Eve (like us) were created in Heavenly Father's image. We look like Heavenly Father.

THOUGHT TREAT: Gingerbread girl and boy.

Activity 28 – Adam and Eve Creation Poster

1. Copy the poster that follows for each child to color.

2. Talk about poster, saying, "Adam and Eve. We are the descendants of Adam and Eve. They were created in the image of Heavenly Father and Jesus."

• Point out that our faces (eyes, nose, mouth, ears), our hair, and our bodies are like their bodies, but we have our own color of hair, eyes, and skin and our own face and body shape. Some of us are taller and some are shorter. Some of us are younger and some are older.

3. Talk about the Home Activity: "Help me realize that the earth and everything on it was created to bring us joy. All we see around us—a star, a flower, an animal—tells us that Heavenly Father and Jesus love us!"

THOUGHT TREAT: Image cookies. Cut out people-shaped cookies, then bake and frost. Talk about why we're thankful for our bodies of flesh and bones that help us walk, talk, help, and play.

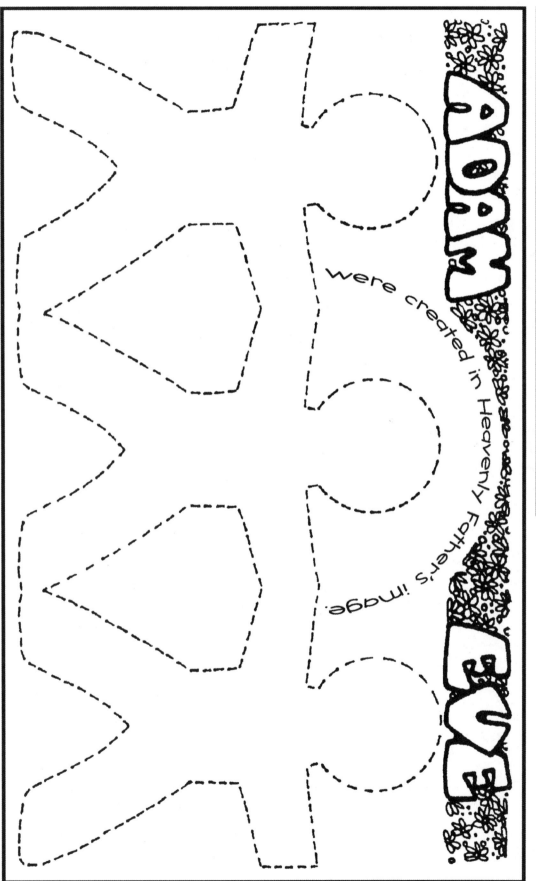

ADAM

EVE

were created in Heavenly Father's image.

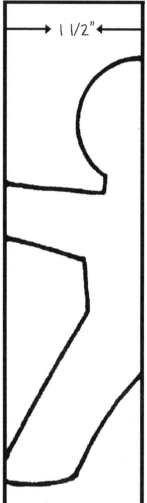

1 1/2"

Fold 6 times

Adam and Eve

They were created in the image of Heavenly Father and Jesus.

We are the descendants of Adam and Eve.

 **Home Activity:** Help me to realize that the earth and everything on it was created to bring us joy. All that we see around us—a star, a flower, an animal—tells us that Heavenly Father and Jesus love us!

LESSON 15   THEME: The Sabbath Is a Day of Worship

1. Present lesson on p. 45–47 in the *Primary 1 Sunbeam* manual to help children realize that the Sabbath day is a day of worship and rest, where we remember Heavenly Father and Jesus. It is a commandment from Heavenly Father to keep Sunday—the Sabbath day—holy.

2. Present both or one of the following activities to help teach the lesson visually.

3. Sing with children. Sing "Saturday" (*Children's Songbook*, 196). For fun action ideas, go to the same song in the *Super Little Singers* book (160) or CD-ROM.

Activity 29 – Sunday Is a Day of Rest – Creation Collar

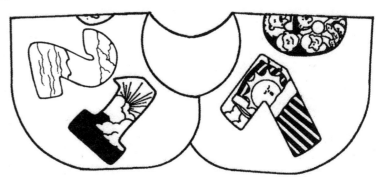

1. Copy the collar parts A and B that follow for each child. Mount parts together and place around child's neck.

2. Talk to children about the days of creation on the collar telling them of the seventh day, a day of rest.

THOUGHT TREAT: Day 7 cookie (cut out sugar cookies in the shape of a *7* for the seventh day of creation or an *S* for Sabbath or Sunday, and bake). Children may have fun frosting the cookie and decorating them with colored candies. QUICK-TO-MAKE OPTION: Make pancakes in days 1–7 shapes. Top with honey butter (mix 1/4 part honey with 3/4 part butter or peanut butter).

Activity 30 – Sabbath Special Day Poster

1. Copy the poster that follows for each child to color.

2. Talk about poster, saying, "The Sabbath day is a special day!"

• "I am happy when I go to church on Sunday to learn about Jesus." Show a picture of Jesus and tell a story about Him. "We learn to make right choices so we can be happy and live with Jesus again someday."

• "I am happy when I spend time with my family on Sunday." Children can share their favorite Sunday family activities (maybe ask parents ahead of time).

• "I am happy when I can rest on Sunday." Discuss ways to rest on the Sabbath.

3. Talk about the Home Activity: "Praise me when I do the right things on Sunday. Help me do work on Saturday so I can be ready for Sunday."

THOUGHT TREAT: Sabbath smoothie. Blend ice with juice to create a smoothie. Give children a straw to drink it as they talk about smooth (good)—Sabbath day things they can do to make the day go smoothly.

Part A

Part B

Attach Part A Here

The Sabbath day is a special day!

I am happy when I go to church on Sunday to learn about Jesus.

I am happy when I spend time with my family on Sunday.

I am happy when I can rest on Sunday.

Home Activity: Praise me when I do the right things on Sunday. Help me do my work on Saturday so I can be ready for Sunday.

LESSON 16   THEME: *I Have a Body*

1. Present lesson on p. 48–51 in the *Primary 1 Sunbeam* manual to help children appreciate and respect their physical bodies that Heavenly Father game them.

2. Present both or one of the following activities to help teach the lesson visually.

3. Sing with children. Sing "Head, Shoulders, Knees, and Toes," "Hinges," and "Once There Was a Snowman" (or "Once I was a Baby") (*Children's Songbook*, 275, 277, 249). For fun action activities, go to the same songs in the *Super Little Singers* book (158, 159) or CD-ROM.

Activity 31 – Good Food Makes Me Strong – Feeding Daniel Good Food

1. Copy the Daniel poster and food items that follow for each child. Cut a slit in Daniel's mouth to insert food. Glue Daniel poster to separate piece of paper, gluing sides and bottom only and leaving room for food to drop into the pocket. To retrieve food, simply separate top and reach in.

2. As children learn of the story of Daniel, who ate good food for a healthy body, they can put good food into Daniel's mouth. Food items shown are nuts, corn, water, bread, rice, and wheat cakes. See story on page 49 in the Primary manual as you tell of Daniel, who ate the food Heavenly Father wanted him to eat. (See also Daniel 1.)

THOUGHT TREAT: Healthy foods. Share a variety of tempting good-for-you foods (e.g., apples, celery with peanut butter, cheese sticks, dried fruit, pretzels, or bananas).

Activity 32 – I Love My Body Poster

1. Copy the poster that follows for each child to color.

2. Talk about poster, saying, "I love my body! Heavenly Father gave me this wonderful gift to care for and protect."

• "We can eat and taste many wonderful foods! What is your favorite thing to eat?" Share something you like to eat.

• "We can do many things with our hands. What do you like to do?" Show children how to cut out a smiley face drawn on paper.

• "Our eyes can see many things. What do you love to see?" Look out the window or at a picture to find things in the picture.

• "Our ears let us enjoy so many beautiful sounds. What do you love to hear?" Tweet like a bird, blow to make wind sound, sniffle nose to make the sound of breathing in.

3. Talk about the Home Activity: "Listen as I tell you about what I can do with my eyes, ears, mouth, hands, and feet."

THOUGHT TREAT: About-face crackers. Have children create a face on a round cracker with cheese from a spray can. Tell what eyes, ears, and mouths can do. Talk about the hands the children used to make the face, the feet they used to walk to the table, and the mouth they used to eat the cracker.

ate good food for a healthy body.

♡ I love my body! ♡

Heavenly Father gave me this wonderful gift to care for and protect.

We can eat and taste many wonderful foods! What is your favorite thing to eat?

We can do many things with our hands. What do you like to do?

Our eyes can see many things. What do you love to see?

Our ears let us enjoy so many beautiful sounds. What do you love to hear?

Home Activity: Listen as I tell you about what I can do with my eyes, ears, mouth, hands, and feet.

LESSON 17   THEME: *I Am Thankful for My Hands*

1. Present lesson on p. 52–56 in the *Primary 1 Sunbeam* manual to help children appreciate their hands and what they can do.

2. Present both or one of the following activities to help teach the lesson visually.

3. Sing these songs with children. Sing "Hinges" (*Children's Songbook*, 277). For fun activities, see *Super Little Singers* (158). During the song, have children move wrists to show where hands are hooked on. Sing "Eensy Weensy Spider" in *Super Little Singers* (visual on p. 2, words and music on p. 195). Use fingers to show spider crawling up arm. Sing "Five Little Ducks" in *Super Little Singer* (visuals on p. 33, words and music on p. 196). Use the whole hand, putting fingers down as ducks go away, then raising them up when five little ducks return. Open/close whole hand as mother and father ducks quack.

Activity 33 – My Hands Can Help! – Helping Hand Mitten

1. Copy the mitten that follows for each child. Cut out and glue mitten together 1/4" on outside edge, leaving bottom open for child's hand to fit in.

2. Mitten shows children that their hands can help, showing ways they can lend a helping hand: Brush teeth, dress, play ball, wash face, eat, feed cat, and make music. Children slip mitten over their hand and flip mitten back and forth to show ways they can help. The smile reminds children that helping makes them happy. Ask children to come up one at a time and tell others ways their hands can help.

THOUGHT TREAT: Thumbprint or handprint cookie. Roll cookie dough into balls and press a child's handprint or thumbprint into cookie dough. Sprinkle hand or thumbprint with colored sugar or decorator candies before baking. As children eat their cookie, remind them that Heavenly Father and Jesus created our hands so we could use them to work, play, and get ready for church.

Activity 34 – My Hands Poster

1. Copy the poster that follows for each child to color.

2. Talk about poster, saying, "My hands can do many things! Wave, play with my pet, paint, build, zip, bounce, clap, hold. These are my two hands. Aren't they wonderful?"

• Have objects to play with (shown on handout).

• Help children trace their hands onto the blank space (on handout) or place poster paint on a sponge, then inside of hands to make a print of each hand (on handout).

3. Talk about the Home Activity: "Help me understand how many things my hands can do. Let's play catch, make cookies, pop bubbles, or enjoy a game of peek-a-boo!" If time permits, show children how to do these things.

THOUGHT TREAT: Hand cut-out cookie. Cut sugar cookie dough into hand shapes, then bake, frost, and top with jelly beans or tiny candy (for fingernails). Tell children, "Hands are special because they help us _____." Have children name ways they use their hands and help (e.g., brush teeth, dress, play ball, wash face, play drums, eat, feed pet, set the table, dust the blinds, shine mirror, tend baby). (Alternative—hand print in play dough.)

My hands can help!

My hands can do many things!

Wave

Pet

Paint

Build

These are my two hands. Aren't they wonderful?

Zip

Bounce

Clap

Hold

Home Activity: Help me understand how many things my hands can do. Let's play catch, make cookies, pop bubbles, or enjoy a game of peek-a-boo!

LESSON 18   THEME: I Am Thankful for My Ears

1. Present lesson on p. 57–59 in the *Primary 1 Sunbeam* manual to help children appreciate their ears and what they can do.

2. Present both or one of the following activities to help teach the lesson visually.

3. Sing with children. Sing "Old McDonald." For fun visuals, music, and lyrics, go to the same song in the *Super Little Singers* book (101, 198) or CD-ROM. Sing "In the Leafy Treetops" (*Children's Songbook*, 240). For fun actions and a chart to help children sing like a bird, go to the same song in the *Super Little Singers* book (159, 167, 168) or CD-ROM.

Activity 35 – I Am Thankful I Can Hear! – Listen Carefully Rattle

1. Copy the rattle that follows for each child. Fold in half, folding over side and bottom tabs, then glue or tape. Fill 1/3 full with rice, sand, macaroni, popcorn, or beans. Fold top tab and glue. Glue and/or tape a wooden craft stick in the bottom center on back.

2. Children can shake rattle to listen carefully to hear what's inside. This can remind them to thank Heavenly Father for ears that hear.

THOUGHT TREAT: Marshmallow ears. Give each child two marshmallows and a round sugar cookie. Cut marshmallow in half and stick to cookie to look like ears (using frosting as glue). Decorate the eyes, nose, and mouth with frosting in a tube. Child can eat the other marshmallow as they create the face cookie. Talk about the things you can hear with your ears and then eat the cookie. Things you might hear: Mother's voice, Father telling you to say your prayers, your teacher saying, "Be reverent," your dog barking because he needs some food, and the birds chirping.

Activity 36 – Thankful Ears Poster

1. Copy the poster that follows for each child to color.

2. Talk about poster, saying, "My ears are such a blessing! Hear yourself buzz like a bee, ding like a bell, and sing a happy song!"

• Have sounds for children to hear and guess what they are (e.g., wind, buzz, can opening, bell or cell phone ringing, the voice of a mother or father calling).

• Take children for a walk around the church to listen for the sounds of nature: birds singing, bees buzzing, wind blowing, etc. Then sit on the lawn and sing a nature song (see below).

3. Talk about the Home Activity: "Let's experience the many wonderful sounds that our ears can hear. Let's listen to music together, hear a songbird, or hear the words 'I love you.'"

THOUGHT TREAT: Crack, snap, and crunch snacks. Share food that makes a sound when opened or eaten, like cracking a nut, snapping open a banana, or the crunching of cereal when you chew it. Listen for the sounds. Have children listen as you pour water into their cups. Ask them to be quiet before you make the sounds so all can hear. As they eat, have them listen for more sounds: knocking, pounding, clapping, etc.

Fold over side and bottom tabs, then glue or tape.

After filling, fold over top tab and glue.

I am thankful

I can HEAR!

My EARS are such a blessing!

Hear yourself buzz like a bee, ding like a bell, and sing a happy song!

Home Activity: Let's experience the many wonderful sounds that our ears can hear. Let's listen to music together, hear a songbird, or hear the words "I love you."

LESSON 19   THEME: I Am Thankful for My Eyes

1. Present lesson on p. 60–62 in the *Primary 1 Sunbeam* manual to help children appreciate their eyes and what they can do.
2. Present both or one of the following activities to help teach the lesson visually.
3. Sing with children. Sing "Twinkle, Twinkle, Little Star." For fun actions, go to the same song in the *Super Little Singers* book (131) or CD-ROM.

Activity 37 – My Eyes Help Me See – Giant Eyes Headband

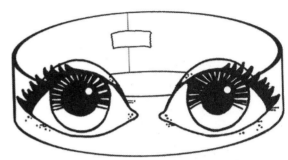

1. Copy the headband that follows for each child. Cut out and tape together, fit headband to child's forehead, and tape or stick together with sticky-back Velcro.
2. The giant eyes on the headband can remind children that their eyes help them see many things: colors, books, stars, flowers, bugs, and motion.

THOUGHT TREAT: Soda crackers with olive eyes and cheese eyelashes. To make, cut an olive in half. Using squeezable cheese, squirt a little cheese in center of cracker and press half an olive into cheese for eye. Squirt strips of cheese around olive to make eyelashes.

Activity 38 – The Eyes Have It! Poster

1. Copy the poster that follows for each child to color.
2. Talk about poster, saying, "The eyes have it! I'm so thankful I can see. Little tiny ladybugs as teensy as can be seem to hide out anywhere. How many can you see?"
• Help children color ladybugs red.
• Recite the nursery rhyme: "Ladybug! Ladybug! Fly away home." For older children, you can add the rest: "Your house is on fire, and your children all gone. All except one, and that's little Ann, for she crept under the frying pan."
3. Talk about the Home Activity: "Help me look into the mirror to see my eyes. Show me how they move, blink, open, and close (show them in the mirror). We could take a walk, and you could point out all the wonderful things, both large and very small, that our eyes can see!" (If time permits, take a walk around the meetinghouse to see things you can thank Heavenly Father for.)

THOUGHT TREAT: "Eye" love you eyes-cookie. Place two candy "eyes" on a cookie using frosting. Ask children to tell you why they love their eyes and what they can do. For example, our eyes can see color, clouds, trees, flowers, bugs, birds, family, friends, teachers, pictures, our house, our room, our food, our toys.

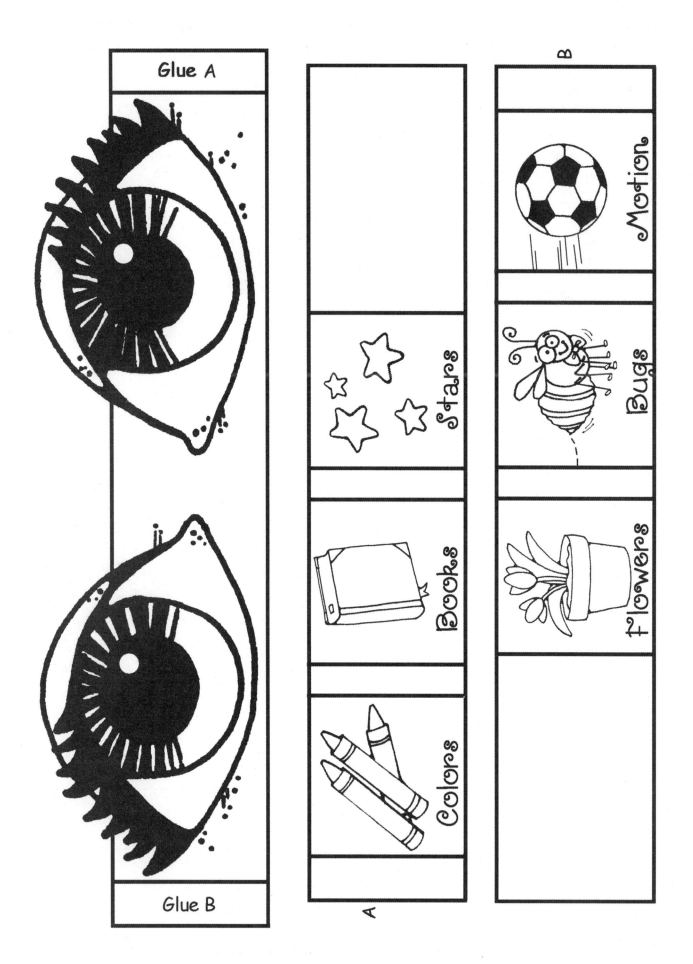

Glue A

Glue B

B

Motion

Bugs

Flowers

Stars

Books

Colors

A

The EYES have it!

Little tiny ladybugs, as teensy as can be, seem to hide out anywhere...how many can you see?

I'm so thankful I can see.

Home Activity: Help me look into the mirror to see my eyes. Show me how they move, blink, open, and close. We could take a walk, and you could point out all the wonderful things, both large and very small, our eyes can see!

LESSON 20   THEME: I Am Thankful That I Can Smell & Taste

1. Present lesson on p. 63–65 in the *Primary 1 Sunbeam* manual to help children appreciate the senses of smell and taste.
2. Present both or one of the following activities to help teach the lesson visually.
3. Sing with children. Sing "Popcorn Popping" (*Children's Songbook*, 242). For fun actions, go to the same song in the *Super Little Singers* book (160) or CD-ROM.

Activity 39 – Heavenly Father created my nose and mouth – Cinnamon Toast Sniff and Taste Test

1. Copy the toast poster that follows for each child. Tape "smell" and "taste" signs over nose and mouth.
2. Visual will help children sniff and taste. To create Sniff and Taste test, have children wet a sponge with water and dampen toast part of image. From a shaker bottle they can sprinkle the wet area of the toast image with cinnamon and sugar (3/4 cup sugar and 1/4 cup cinnamon). Children can smell and taste the cinnamon and sugar. The sugar doesn't come off and it's a great way to show and tell.

THOUGHT TREAT: Cinnamon and sugar toast. Prepare this ahead. Spread butter on bread and sprinkle the cinnamon and sugar mixture (3/4 sugar and 1/4 cinnamon) on top. Toast on broil 2–3 minutes in the oven (not the microwave). Serve bread cold. Encourage children to sniff and taste. *Option:* Sprinkle multicolored decorating candies on top of buttered cinnamon and sugar bread before toasting. Children love to pick at the little candies as they eat.

Activity 40 – I Can Smell and Taste! Poster

1. Copy the poster that follows for each child to color.
2. Talk about poster, saying, "I can smell and taste!
—Can you think of something that tastes sour? (e.g., lemons, limes, pickles)
—What animal uses scent to warn his enemies? (Skunk)
—What can you think of that smells or tastes sweet?"
(flowers, Mom's perfume, Grandma's hugs, watermelon, berries, hot bread, cookies, oranges)
3. Talk about the Home Activity: "Let's go find many different things that we can smell and taste. We could taste salty, sweet, and sour foods and smell each of them too!"
• Share some salty chips, popcorn, or a pickle and a sweet banana or treat.

THOUGHT TREAT: Orange-you-glad-you-can-smell-and-taste? oranges. Peel a small orange for each child and have them smell the citrus scent. Then say, "Orange" (aren't) you glad you can smell and taste?" As they eat each section, have them tell you a reason they are glad they can smell and taste.

Heavenly Father created my nose and mouth.

Fold back and glue on dotted line.

Taste

Fold and glue.

Smell

I can smell and taste!

Can you think of something that tastes sour?

What animal uses scent to warn his enemies?

What can you think of that smells and tastes sweet?

 **Home Activity:** Let's go find many different things that we can smell and taste. We could taste salty, sweet, and sour foods, and smell each of them too!

LESSON 21   THEME: I Have Feelings

1. Present lesson on p. 66–70 in the *Primary 1 Sunbeam* manual to help children understand and identify feelings and learn ways to be happy.

2. Present both or one of the following activities to help teach the lesson visually.

3. Sing with children. Sing "Smiles," "I Am Like a Star," and "Jesus Wants Me for a Sunbeam" (*Children's Songbook*, 267, 163, 60). For fun visuals, go to the same songs in the *Super Little Singers* book (102, 61, 62) or CD-ROM. Sing "If You're Happy" (*Children's Songbook*, 266). For fun actions, go to the same song in the *Super Little Singers* book (159) or CD-ROM.

Activity 41 – Sunshine Face – Smile/Frown Flip-flag

1. Copy the flag that follows for each child. Glue a wooden stick or an unsharpened pencil in the bottom center. Fold flag and glue back to back.

2. With this Smile/Frown flip-flag, children can flip back and forth to learn about their feelings and know that it's more fun to have a sunshine face. To flip the flag, move it back and forth quickly to try and see both sides at once.

THOUGHT TREAT: Smiley-face cookies.

Activity 42 – I Have Many Feelings! Poster

1. Copy the poster that follows for each child to color.

2. Talk about poster, saying, "I have many feelings!" (happy, frightened, angry, sad)

• Talk about experiences children have that bring on these feelings and what they can do to feel better.

3. Talk about the Home Activity: "Ask me to tell you when I am happy, sad, angry, or frightened. Help me thank Heavenly Father when I am happy. Help me pray so the Holy Ghost can help me feel better when I feel sad, angry, or frightened."

• See lesson 4 Prayer poster to review how to pray.

THOUGHT TREAT: Feeling-face cookies. Give each child two cookies, one frosted with a smile and the other with a frown. As they eat each cookie, talk about feelings that come with that expression: smile (happy) and frown (angry, sad). Give them a mirror so they can try expressions. Show them how to look surprised (mouth open). The best expression is a smile that comes from making right choices. Sing "Smiles" (above) to turn frown upside-down and smile the frown away.

I have many feelings!

happy

frightened

Can you make a happy face?

Can you make a sad face?

angry

sad

Can you make a scared face?

Home Activity: Ask me to tell you when I am happy, sad, angry, or frightened. Help me thank Heavenly Father when I am happy. Help me pray so the Holy Ghost can help me feel better when I feel sad, angry, or frightened.

LESSON 22   THEME: I Can Do Many Things

1. Present lesson on p. 71–73 in the *Primary 1 Sunbeam* manual to help children know that as children of Heavenly Father we can do many things.
2. Present both or one of the following activities to help teach the lesson visually.
3. Sing with children. Sing "Fun to Do," "Do As I'm Doing," and "I Am a Child of God" (*Children's Songbook*, 253, 276, 2). For fun visuals, go to the same songs in the *Super Little Singers* book (34, 2, 34) or CD-ROM.
• Sing "Once There Was a Snowman" (*Children's Songbook*, 249). For fun activity, go to the same song in the *Super Little Singers* book (159) or CD-ROM. You can change the word "snowman" to "giant" (compare this to the giant, Goliath, who fell down when hit by David's stone).

Activity 43 – I Can See, Hear, Smell – String of I "Can" Dos

1. Copy the cans that follow for each child.
2. To make, lay a 20" piece of string on the back center of each can. At the same time, glue the matching sticker over the back of the can (over the string). Matching stickers: Flower (I Can Smell), Apple (I Can Taste), Airplane (I Can See), and Bird (I Can Hear).
3. With string of cans, children can turn cans over to see images on the back, showing them how they can use the senses Heavenly Father gave them to do many things.

THOUGHT TREAT: Treats in a can. Enlarge labels (shown left) and place on empty cans to enclose treats to use week after week. Open cans with safety-edge can opener. Use larger cans for graham crackers, soda crackers, cereal, and/or dried fruit. The cans will remind children each week of the things they "can" do.

Activity 44 – I can do . . . (David & Goliath) Poster

1. Copy the poster that follows for each child to color.
2. <u>Talk about poster</u>, saying, "I can do so many things!" (1 Samuel 17). Tell the story of David and Goliath. "Even though David was only a small boy and Goliath was so big, Heavenly Father helped David do a very difficult thing. Heavenly Father will help us too."
• Talk about hard things to do: not tall enough to reach things, not knowing how to do things, making friends, learning to tie your shoe.
• Talk about things children can do: help my family, eat by myself, make my bed, pick up my toys, hang up my clothes, fix my food, clean up after I eat or play, get my seat belt on, tie my shoes, smile, give a hug, take a bath, wash my hair, get dressed, say my prayers.
3. <u>Talk about the Home Activity</u>: "Help me to know the many things I can do. Help me realize that Heavenly Father and Jesus will help me do things that are difficult."

THOUGHT TREAT: Spirit-and-body cookie. Give children an unfrosted body-shaped cookie. Tell them, "Our bodies can do many things with Heavenly Father's help." As they watch, frost a dot on the cookie's forehead and a heart on the chest. Tell them that Heavenly Father loves us so He gave us our mind and heart. Like David, we can pray for help. The Holy Ghost gives us ideas and feelings so we will know what to do.

I can do so many things!

1 Samuel 17

Even though David was only a small boy and Goliath was so big. Heavenly Father helped David do a very difficult thing. Heavenly Father will help me too.

 **Home Activity:** Help me know the many things I can do. Help me realize that Heavenly Father and Jesus will help me do things that are difficult.

LESSON 23   THEME: I Belong to a Family

1. Present lesson on p. 74–77 in the *Primary 1 Sunbeam* manual to help children understand that Heavenly Father planned for us each to belong to a family that needs us and loves us.
2. Present both or one of the following activities to help teach the lesson visually.
3. Sing with children. Sing "A Happy Family," "When We're Helping," and "Quickly I'll Obey" (*Children's Songbook*, 198a, 198b, 197). For fun visuals, go to the same songs in the *Super Little Singers* book (1, 102, 132) or CD-ROM.

Activity 45 – I Am Part of a Family – Family Face Block Game

1. Copy the block that follows for each child. Choose the block that fits the boy or girl or nationality (if printing in color from the CD-ROM). To make, fold and glue edges and tape down lid.
2. To help children feel they are part of a family, use the Family Face block to play a game. *To Play:* Have children take turns rolling block and telling something about a member of their family as the family member appears on the block (face up). *Ideas:* Tell what that family member has taught you, why you love them, or how you can help and show love to that person. When child rolls "I Am Part of a Family," he/she says, "I love my family."

THOUGHT TREAT: Pretzel family necklace. String pretzels on yarn or ribbon for child to wear home. As they eat this yummy treat, they'll think, "My family's really neat!"

Activity 46 – Great Family Poster

1. Copy the poster that follows for each child to color.
2. Talk about poster, saying, "I belong to a great family! We will make our journey together. Heavenly Father planned for me to belong to a family that loves me."
• Have children tell you something they love about their family.
• Ask them how they help their family to be happy.
3. Talk about the Home Activity: "Let's talk about ways we can be a happy family. Show me one thing I can do that will contribute to our family and help others to be happy."

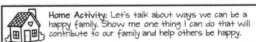

Home Activity: Let's talk about ways we can be a happy family. Show me one thing I can do that will contribute to our family and help others be happy.

THOUGHT TREAT: Heartbeat cookies. Give children a cookie with an unwrapped candy kiss in the center. To place candy on cookie, glue on with frosting or press into freshly baked peanut butter cookie. Tell children that our heart (point to the candy kiss) beats inside our chest each day to keep us alive. This heart can also feel love for our family each day to keep us happy. Open candy kiss and talk about ways to open our heart and show love to our family (e.g., say I love you, give a hug, share, and help).

We will make our journey together. ♡

I belong to a great family!

Heavenly Father planned for me to belong to a family that loves me.

 **Home Activity:** Let's talk about ways we can be a happy family. Show me one thing I can do that will contribute to our family and help others be happy.

LESSON 24   THEME: I Love My Brothers & Sisters

1. Present lesson on p. 78–80 in the *Primary 1 Sunbeam* manual to encourage children to show love for their brothers and sisters.
2. Present both or one of the following activities to help teach the lesson visually.
3. Sing with children. Sing "A Happy Family" and "Jesus Said Love Everyone" (*Children's Songbook*, 198, 61). For fun visuals, go to the same songs in the *Super Little Singers* book (1, 62) or CD-ROM. Sing "Popcorn Popping" (*Children's Songbook*, 242). For fun action ideas, go to the same song in the *Super Little Singers* book (160) or CD-ROM.

Activity 47 – Brothers & Sisters Help – Baby Moses in the Bulrushes

1. Copy the baby Moses scene that follows for each child. Cut a slit in the basket to enclose baby. Slide into basket.
2. Using the baby Moses in the Bulrushes scene, you can show children how a sister helped her brother (Exodus 1:22–2:10). Move figures around to tell the story. Tell how Miriam, the baby's sister, watched over her baby brother until he was safe. Then tell how the Pharaoh's daughter saved Moses from danger (Exodus 2:1–10).

THOUGHT TREAT: Smiling family fudge. Make some fudge by melting in the microwave 2 minutes at a time: 1 package sweetened chocolate chips, ½ can sweetened and condensed milk, and 1 teaspoon vanilla. Stir and form into round flattened pieces making a spoon-edge smile and add candies for eyes. Talk about how happy our family is when we help them.

Activity 48 – Love My Brothers & Sisters Poster

1. Copy the poster that follows for each child to color.
2. <u>Talk about poster</u>, helping children memorize it: "I love my brothers and sisters! I can be a popcorn brother or sister! I will quickly 'pop' up to help, 'pop' a smile, or 'pop' out my arms for a loving hug."
• Around a bowl of popcorn (see TREAT below), talk to children about sharing by saying, "What if I popped this bowl of popcorn and decided to eat it all by myself without sharing it with you? Would this be showing love?"
• Ask, "What are some ways we can show love to our family?" (Help, smile, give hugs [see handout], be kind, share toys, say please and thank you, say I love you, feed pets, pick up toys, make our bed, clean our room, put our clothes away, clean up our messes, ask how we can help, be reverent during family prayer, listen during family home evening.)
3. <u>Talk about the Home Activity</u>: "Let's talk about all the ways I can show love and help my brothers and sisters. Let's learn how to do a group hug and express our love."

THOUGHT TREAT: Popcorn treats. Share a bowl of popcorn on serving napkins. Talk about sharing. Then have children take turns giving the child next to them a handful of popcorn. Sing "Popcorn" song (above).

I love my brothers and sisters!

I can be a popcorn brother or sister! I will quickly "pop" up to help, "pop" a smile, or "pop" out my arms for a loving hug.

Home Activity: Let's talk about all the ways I can show love and help my brothers and sisters. Let's learn how to do a group hug and express our love.

LESSON 25   THEME: I Love My Whole Family

1. Present lesson on p. 81–83 in the *Primary 1 Sunbeam* manual to help children feel love for all family members.
2. Present both or one of the following activities to help teach the lesson visually.
3. Sing with children. Sing "A Happy Family" and "Quickly I'll Obey" (*Children's Songbook*, 198, 197). For fun visuals, go to the same songs in the *Super Little Singers* book (1, 102) or CD-ROM.

Activity 49 – I Love My Whole Family - Family Ties Necklace or Belt

1. Copy the family blocks that follow for each child. Punch holes and tread the yarn through blocks, leaving enough yarn to tie on as a necklace or belt.
2. Encourage children to talk about family members of immediate family and relatives too. Tell children that it is important to love their whole family, pray for them, spend time with them, and tell them they love them.

THOUGHT TREAT: Rope licorice tied in knots. Knot two pieces of licorice together. Tell children that this knot in the licorice helps keep the pieces together. Telling your family that you love them is one way to strengthen family ties and "tie" families more securely together.

Activity 50 – I Love My Whole Family - Poster

1. Copy the poster that follows for each child to color.
2. Talk about poster, saying, "I love my whole family! I am a little acorn, one of many you can see! And every little acorn comes from the old oak tree!"
• Help children feel that everyone on their family tree is important. You could even spotlight someone from their family tree (with a photo to show and tell).
• Show photos of your family members, telling who they are and why they are important to you. Ask children to tell you something about their family and why they love them (see "Thought Treat" below).
3. Talk about the Home Activity: "Show me pictures of my family and tell me who they are. Let's chat about each person and write them a letter or card or call or visit them."

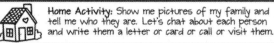

THOUGHT TREAT: Family-in-a-heartbeat pretzels. Give children a few heart-shaped (knotted) pretzels, one for each family member. Tell children that when you love someone, your heart feels a special feeling. As children eat the heart-shaped pretzels, have them tell you about their family and why they love them. You can even string pretzels onto licorice or ribbon to make a necklace or bracelet.

Aunt. Grandpa. Uncle. Grandma. Mom. Cousin. Dad. Me.

I'm a little acorn, one of many you can see!

And every little acorn comes from the old oak tree!

I love my whole family!

Home Activity: Show me pictures of my family and tell me who they are. Let's chat about each person and write them a letter or card or call or visit them.

LESSON 26   THEME: Families Can Be Together Forever

1. Present lesson on p. 84–88 in the *Primary 1 Sunbeam* manual to help each child understand that temples are sacred places where families can be sealed together forever and then encourage them to prepare to enter the temple.

2. Present both or one of the following activities to help teach the lesson visually.

3. Sing with children. Sing "Families Can Be Together Forever" (*Children's Songbook*, 188).

Activity 51 – Preparing for the Temple – Temple Tie and Tithing Purse

1. Copy tie and purse images that follow for each child. To make the Temple Tie and Tithing Purse, fold purse in half and glue together on sides and bottom, leaving top open. Punch holes where indicated to attach string for tie and string-strap to purse.

2. Use images to show children how families can prepare to go to the temple. Talk about tithing by moving coins in and out of purse.

THOUGHT TREAT: Money candies wrapped in gold foil, coin-shaped candies to count out one tenth, or use temple-shaped mints.

Activity 52 – Families Together Forever Poster

1. Copy the poster that follows for each child to color.

2. Talk about poster, saying, "Families can be together forever. The temple is a sacred place where we are sealed together."

• Talk about forever families as follows:

—Show a copy of handout cut into puzzle pieces (cutting out family members separately).

—Say, "When parents are married in the temple, they are sealed to each other and their children" (put puzzle together).

—Take away one family member and place in an envelope as you say, "When we die, we are separated for a while, but we can have joy knowing we are sealed in the temple." (Seal envelope by taping it shut.)

—"After we are resurrected, we can be with our family again." (Unseal envelope and have children put puzzle together again.)

• Talk about ways children can prepare for the temple: keep Word of Wisdom (eat good foods), pay tithing (to help build temples), pray (to stay close to Heavenly Father), go to church (to learn about the gospel), love others (live the teachings of Jesus), obey parents (love our family).

• Show pictures of temples and talk about them, telling how a temple is Heavenly Father's house, where He visits.

3. Talk about the Home Activity: "Let's look at a book about temples and talk about how wonderful it is to be together forever. If a temple is close, let's go see the temple!"

THOUGHT TREAT: Happy-heart cookie. Frost a smile on a heart-shaped cookie for each child. Say that because they love their family so much, they will want to be sealed in the temple to be with them forever.

I can pay
Tithing.

I earn a dime,
My world is fine;
I pay a penny,
My blessings are many!

Families Can Be Together Forever

The temple is a sacred place...

...where we are sealed together.

 Home Activity: Let's look at a book about temples and talk about how wonderful it is to be together forever. If a temple is close, let's go see the temple!

LESSON 27   THEME: We Can Pray As a Family

1. Present lesson on p. 89–91 in the *Primary 1 Sunbeam* manual to help children understand that regular family prayer helps keep a family close to Heavenly Father and to each others.
2. Present both or one of the following activities to help teach the lesson visually.
3. Sing with children. Sing "My Heavenly Father Loves Me" (*Children's Songbook*, 228). For fun visuals, go to the same song in the *Super Little Singers* book (101) or CD-ROM.

Activity 53 – Heart-to-Heart – Family Prayer Chart

1. Copy the prayer chart that follows for each child. Cut slits in day pockets (lines above days). Count the number of people in child's family and cut out and paper-punch a heart for each family member. Write the child's name on one of the hearts. Punch a hole to the left of chart. Before punching a hole, put a piece of tape behind the designated location to prevent tearing once the strings are attached. Tie a string to each heart (one for each member of the child's family). Tie strings to chart. Show children how to place their heart/name in their assigned day pocket.
2. Children can place family names on the hearts. Then during the week, from Monday to Sunday, they can place family-hearts in the day's pocket to show who is giving the family prayer. Talk about the happy feelings we have when we pray together. Show children how to have a family prayer.

THOUGHT TREAT: Heart-shaped cookies or candies.

Activity 54 – Family Prayer Poster

1. Copy the poster that follows for each child to color.
2. Talk about poster, saying, "We love to have family prayer! We pray together to express our thanks, to ask for what we need, and to show our love for each other."
• Talk about things we can pray about (some on handout), asking children what they would say. Objects can be passed to each child so they can show them as they talk (e.g., picture of a family; food; scriptures; pictures of Jesus, a meetinghouse, a temple; money or purse/wallet). Say, "Heavenly Father wants us to pray to Him in the name of Jesus Christ. We can thank Him and ask for blessings."
3. Talk about the Home Activity: "Talk to me about family prayer and ask me what I want to pray about. Then help me say family prayer often so I can feel close to Heavenly Father and my family."

THOUGHT TREAT: Family-prayer popsicle. Treat children to a popsicle. Each popsicle represents a person having family prayer. Have children point their popsicle into the circle to show that families get together to pray. Then have a prayer together to thank Heavenly Father and ask for blessings. Ask children to tell things they say in family prayer (e.g., "Bless Grandpa and Grandma.").

We love to have family prayer!

Home
Food
Gospel
Temple
Earth
Jesus

Book of Mormon

Commandments
Choose the Right
Love
School
Direction
Finances

We pray together to express our thanks, to ask for what we need, and to show our love for each other.

Home Activity: Talk to me about family prayer and ask me what I want to pray about. Then help me say family prayer often so I can feel close to Heavenly Father and my family.

LESSON 28   THEME: I Can Be Obedient

1. Present lesson on p. 92–94 in the *Primary 1 Sunbeam* manual to strengthen each child's desire to obey Heavenly Father and Jesus Christ and to obey his or her parents.

2. Present both or one of the following activities to help teach the lesson visually.

3. Sing with children. Sing "Quickly I'll Obey" (*Children's Songbook*, 197). For fun visuals, go to the same song in the *Super Little Singers* book (102) or CD-ROM.

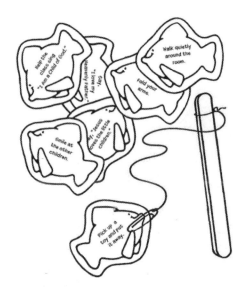

Activity 55 – Obedient – Fishes & Wishes to Obey

1. Copy the fish that follow for each child. Make fishing pole by tying and taping a string to the end of a wooden craft stick. Attach a paperclip at the other end of string. Don't color over fish words, just the edge of fish or color with light markers.

2. Go fish*, with one or two sets of fish, helping children fish to find fun ways to obey. Talk about actions as they throw a string (with a paperclip attached) over a chair to find a fish. Tell children that Heavenly Father wants us to obey. Let's get some fishes to find out the wishes.

*To Fish. Hook a paperclip to the end of the fishing pole. Child can cast his/her pole over a chair. Place fish on paperclip to pull back. Read and do the action with the children.

THOUGHT TREAT: Fish crackers or gummy fish.

Activity 56 – Obedience Poster

1. Copy the poster that follows for each child to color.

2. Talk about poster, saying, "I can be obedient. When my mother/father calls (call out) me, quickly (clap hands) I'll obey!"

• Talk about things parents might ask children to do: pick up toys; make bed; wash face; brush teeth; comb hair; say prayers; go to sleep; be nice; say please, thank you, and excuse me; help at home; don't touch; don't hit, kick, or push; be reverent.

3. Talk about the Home Activity: "Tell me ways I can be obedient. Help me understand why, and praise me when I do."

THOUGHT TREAT: Obedience orange. Peel several oranges and split each between two children. Have children pull segments apart, and as they eat each piece, name ways they can obey. Say, "We can trust that what Heavenly Father and our parents ask us to do is right. When we obey them, we will be happy."

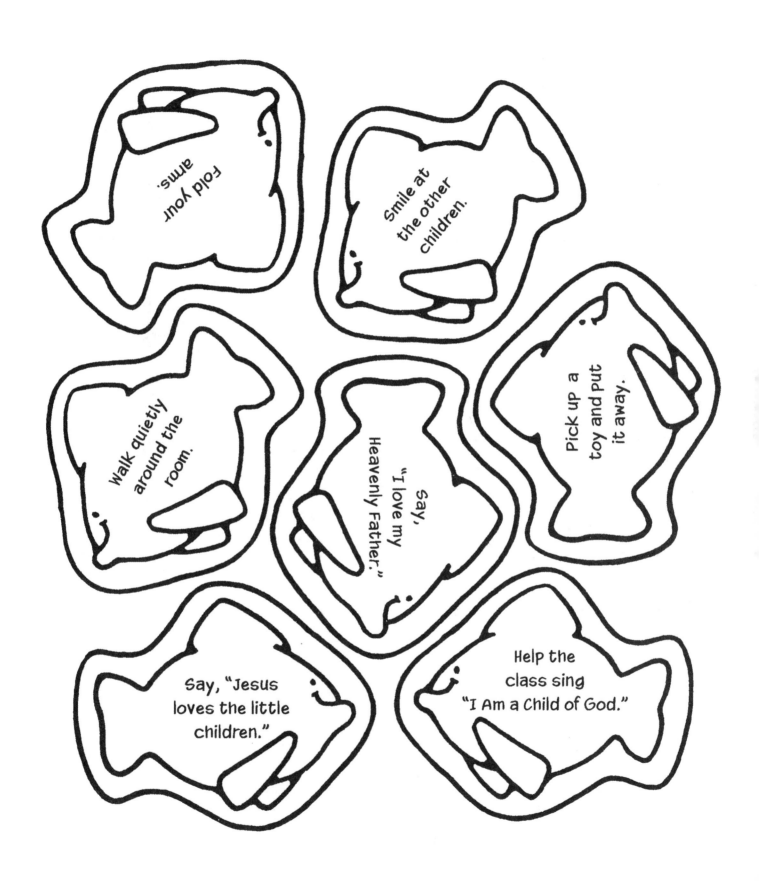

Fold your arms.

Smile at the other children.

Walk quietly around the room.

Say, "I love my Heavenly Father."

Pick up a toy and put it away.

Say, "Jesus loves the little children."

Help the class sing "I Am a Child of God."

When my mother  me, I'll obey!

When my father me, I'll obey!

I can be obedient.

Home Activity: Tell me ways that I can be obedient. Help me to understand why, and praise me when I do.

LESSON 29 THEME: I Can Say I'm Sorry

1. Present lesson on p. 95–97 in the *Primary 1 Sunbeam* manual to help children understand that when we do something wrong, we should say we are sorry and try to correct the wrong thing we have done.
2. Present both or one of the following activities to help teach the lesson visually.
3. Sing with children. Sing "Jesus Said Love Everyone" (*Children's Songbook*, 61). For fun visuals, go to the same song in the *Super Little Singers* book (62) or CD-ROM.

Activity 57 – I Can Say Hippopotamus. I Can Say I'm Sorry – Hippo Sack Puppet

1. Copy the hippo that follows for each child. Make each child a hippo sack puppet by gluing hippo head on the bottom of a lunch sack, with jaw in the middle of the sack. When fingers move sack flap up and down, the hippo's mouth opens wide as child says, "I'm sorry."
2. Children can enjoy saying I'm sorry with their hippo sack puppet. With the sack, rehearse the word hippopotamus. If they can say this long word, they can say I'm sorry when they do something wrong.

THOUGHT TREAT: Animal-shaped cookies to look for hippos!

Activity 58 – Say "Sorry" Poster

1. Copy the poster that follows for each child to color.
2. Talk about poster, saying, "I can say I'm sorry. When I have done something wrong, I can say I'm sorry and do my best to make it right."
• Play Red Light, Green Light, using the singing motivator signs in the *Super Little Singers* book (168) or CD-ROM. Talk about stopping when an action is not right and going when the action is right.
• Give children a card and have them tear it in half, then have them mend it with tape. Compare this with doing something wrong and mending it by saying sorry and asking for forgiveness.
3. Talk about the Home Activity: "Help me know when I have done something wrong, but at the same time, help me know how to fix it. I want to choose the right so I can be like Jesus and please my Heavenly Father."

THOUGHT TREAT: Peek-a-boo roll-ups. Talk about the tears we shed when we know we have done wrong. Say, "Sometimes it is hard to say sorry when we have done wrong." Give each child a fruit roll-up and have them roll it out and place it in front of their faces. Have children peak out from behind the roll-up and say, "I'm sorry." Talk about actions that make them frown and actions that make them smile.

I can say I'm sorry.

When I have done something wrong, I can say I'm sorry and do my best to make it right.

Home Activity: Help me know when I have done something wrong, but at the same time, help me know how to fix it. I want to choose the right so I can be like Jesus and please my Heavenly Father.

LESSON 30   THEME: I Can Forgive Others

1. Present lesson on p. 98–100 in the *Primary 1 Sunbeam* manual to encourage children to be forgiving.
2. Present both or one of the following activities to help teach the lesson visually.
3. Sing with children. Sing "Jesus Said Love Everyone" and "Smiles" (*Children's Songbook*, 61, 267). For fun visuals, go to the same songs in the *Super Little Singers* book (62, 102) or CD-ROM.

Activity 59 – Jesus Wants Us to Forgive – Joseph and Brothers Finger Puppets

1. Copy the puppets that follow for each child. Roll puppets around a pencil to curl into shape. Tape the back and slip puppets over fingers.
2. Have children place this set of Joseph and Brothers finger puppets on their fingers to act out the story of Joseph, who was sold into Egypt but forgave his brothers.

THOUGHT TREAT: Bread or crackers (grain) like the grain Joseph gave his brothers.

Activity 60 – Forgive Others Poster

1. Copy the poster that follows for each child to color.
2. Talk about poster, saying, "I can forgive others!"

• Tell the story of Joseph, who forgave his brothers (in the lesson) and say, "Heavenly Father wants me to forgive others, like Joseph who forgave his brothers and Jesus who forgave others."
• Talk to children about playing with their friends, asking, "Have your friends ever done something to you that made you frown? What was it? Did you forgive them? What if you did something that hurt them and you say sorry. Wouldn't you want them to forgive you?"
3. Talk about the Home Activity: "Help me see that when I am hurt, I can be forgiving. Tell me stories of Jesus and how He taught us to forgive one another."

Home Activity: Help me see that when I am hurt I can be forgiving. Tell me stories of Jesus and how He taught us to forgive one another.

I can forgive others!

THOUGHT TREAT: Hurt frown and happy smile cookie. Frost a cookie with a smile on the top half and a frown on the bottom half, with eyes in the center so you can turn it around to change expression. Turn it as you talk about happy feelings that come when we forgive others and sad feelings that come when we don't. Sing "Smiles," using cookies as a visual, or use visual in *Super Little Singers* book (102).

I can forgive others!

Home Activity: Help me see that when I am hurt I can be forgiving. Tell me stories of Jesus and how He taught us to forgive one another.

LESSON 31 THEME: *I Am Thankful for My Home*

1. Present lesson on p. 101–103 in the *Primary 1 Sunbeam* manual to encourage children to feel gratitude for their home and to help take care of it.

2. Present both or one of the following activities to help teach the lesson visually.

3. Sing with children. Sing "A Happy Family," "When We're Helping," and "Quickly I'll Obey" (*Children's Songbook*, 198, 197). For fun visuals, go to the same songs in the *Super Little Singers* book (1, 102, 132) or CD-ROM.

Activity 61 – Home Sweet Home – Job Jar with Jobs

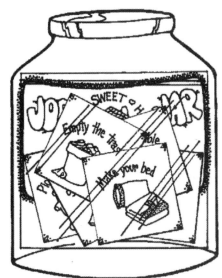

1. Copy the jobs and job jar labels that follow for each child. To make Job jar with Jobs, tape a plastic bag in front of the jar with double-stick tape or rubber-cement glue. Then enclose jobs and treats.

2. Job jar will help children learn ways they can do their jobs to take care of their home. Place reward treats (see below) that they can draw and eat to remind them that helping at home is really neat.

THOUGHT TREAT: Reward treats—Supply six treats to place in a bag to whet their appetite for a job well done. Tell the children that they are to be honest and not eat a piece of candy until one of the jobs found in the job jar is done.

Activity 62 – Thankful for Home Poster

1. Copy the poster that follows for each child to color.

2. Talk about poster, saying, "I'm so thankful for my home! I can pick up my own toys. I can wipe up my own spills. I can help set the table for dinner. I can be cheerful and happy."

• Play follow the leader by demonstrating the above actions and asking children to copy you. Children can take turns being the leader. More Ideas: spray and wipe a window or wall, pick up trash, turn out lights, tend brother or sister, help Grandma and Grandpa, straighten the rug, feed pet, sweep, dust.

3. Talk about the Home Activity: "Teach me what I can do to help at home and love my family. Then I can feel peaceful and happy as I fill my home with love."

THOUGHT TREAT: Home-sweet-home graham cracker. Create a house by connecting graham-cracker pieces, using frosting from a tube. Say, "Home can be sweet when we help and show love."

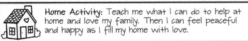

Home Activity: Teach me what I can do to help at home and love my family. Then I can feel peaceful and happy as I fill my home with love.

Set the table

Sweep the floor

Make your bed

Pick up your toys

Empty the trash

Fold your clothes

I can wipe up my own spills.

❤ I can help set the table for dinner.

❤ I can pick up my own toys.

❤ I can be cheerful and happy.

I'm so thankful for my home!

Home Activity: Teach me what I can do to help at home and love my family. Then I can feel peaceful and happy as I fill my home with love.

LESSON 32 THEME: I Am Thankful for Food & Clothing

1. Present lesson on p. 104–106 in the *Primary 1 Sunbeam* manual to help children feel and express gratitude for food and clothing.
2. Present both or one of the following activities to help teach the lesson visually.
3. Sing with children. Sing "Popcorn Popping" (*Children's Songbook*, 242) and "Old McDonald." For fun actions, go to the same songs in the *Super Little Singers* book (101, 160) or CD-ROM.

Activity 63 – Thankful for Food and Clothing – Cupboard and Closet

1. Copy the cupboard/closet card that follows for each child. Fold on line.
2. Cupboard and closet will help children express gratitude for food and clothing. Help them match up and glue food and clothing stickers to the cupboard and closet sides of card.

THOUGHT TREAT: Food (Before eating, have a child thank Heavenly Father for the food and clothing and ask Him to bless the food.)

Activity 64 – Thankful for Food & Clothes Poster

1. Copy the poster that follows for each child to color.
2. Talk about poster, saying, "I'm thankful for food and clothes!" Help children take turns coming up to touch visuals and answer questions as follows:
(1) Starting with the egg on the left, have children answer the question "Do you know where I come from?" Then point to the image on the right that matches: the chicken. (2) Next point to the images on the right, starting with the bee. Ask children the question, "Do you know what I provide?" Then have children find the image on the left that matches: honey.
3. Talk about the Home Activity: "Help me match up food and clothing to know where they came from. Let's talk about how we use plants and animals for food and clothing."

THOUGHT TREAT: Clothing cookies. Cut sugar cookie dough into clothing shapes, then bake and frost. Tell about the flour and sugar you used to make the cookies. Talk about the clothing we wear. Explain how thankful we should be for both our food and clothing.

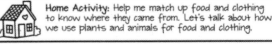

I am thankful for clothes!

I am thankful for food!

MILK

HONEY

I'm thankful for food and clothes!

Do you know where I come from?

Honey

Do you know what I provide?

Home Activity: Help me match up food and clothing to know where they came from. Let's talk about how we use plants and animals for food and clothing.

LESSON 33 THEME: I Can Be a Friend

1. Present lesson on p. 107–110 in the *Primary 1 Sunbeam* manual to help children desire to be a good friend.

2. Present both or one of the following activities to help teach the lesson visually.

3. Sing with children. Sing "Jesus Said Love Everyone" and "Fun to Do" (*Children's Songbook*, 61, 253). For fun visuals, go to the same songs in the *Super Little Singers* book (62, 34) or CD-ROM. Children can use the action cards to show ways they can be a friend (imitate them in the song above). Sing "Do As I'm Doing" (*Children's Songbook*, 276). For fun visuals, go to the same song in the *Super Little Singers* book (2) or CD-ROM. Replace words "Do as I'm doing" with "Be a good friend," and have children do actions like smiling, saying hi, waving, and helping. Children can play follow the leader.

Activity 65 – I Can "Bee" a Friend – Friendship Necklace

1. Copy hearts that follow for each child. Punch holes, tie yarn or ribbon through hearts, and tie at the end.

2. Necklace shows children how to be a friend like Jesus was a friend to others. Help them memorize: I can 'bee' a friend.

THOUGHT TREAT: Heart-shaped cookies.

Activity 66 – "Bee" a Friend Poster

1. Copy the poster that follows for each child to color.

2. Talk about poster, saying, "I can be a friend! Jesus is our loving friend."

• "How many friends do you have? Can you count them?" (See "Thought Treat" below.)

• "How do they know they are your friend?" (Have children tell you kind things they do for their friends, like Jesus when He gathered the children around Him.)

3. Talk about the Home Activity: "Let's name all my friends! Then help me to be kind to my friends at church and at home. Help me to share and say please and thank you."

THOUGHT TREAT: Friendship bracelets. String colored cereal to make a bracelet, telling children: "As you count each color in the bracelet, name your friends one by one: mother, father, brother, sister, grandma, grandpa, teacher, neighbor, nursery friends."

Home Activity: Let's name all my friends! Then help me to be kind to my friends at church and at home. Help me to share and say please and thank you.

I can 🐝 a friend!

How many friends do you have? Can you count them?

How do they know they are your friend?

Jesus is our loving friend.

Home Activity: Let's name all my friends! Then help me to be kind to my friends at church and at home. Help me to share and say please and thank you.

LESSON 34   THEME: I Can Love Others

1. Present lesson on p. 111–114 in the *Primary 1 Sunbeam* manual to encourage children to express love for others through kind words and deeds.
2. Present both or one of the following activities to help teach the lesson visually.
3. Sing with children. Sing "Jesus Said Love Everyone" (*Children's Songbook*, 61). For fun visuals, go to the same song in the *Super Little Singers* book (62) or CD-ROM.

Activity 67 – I Can Share and Care – Good Samaritan Show-and-Tell

1. Copy the Good Samaritan scene that follows for each child. Attach movable arm on picture with a paper fastener. Glue story on the back of picture.
2. Help children use the scene to tell the story that Jesus told (Luke 10:30–37). Move the hand holding the cup up and down to give the man a drink. Tell children that Heavenly Father wants us to love others.

THOUGHT TREAT: Water and Samaritan snacks. Share with children bread and fruit. Tell them this is like the food the Good Samaritan shared with the person in need. He showed his love for others. Talk about what children can do to be Good Samaritans (e.g., share their toys and food, smile, and be nice).

Activity 68 – Love Others Poster

1. Copy the poster that follows for each child to color.
2. <u>Talk about poster</u>, saying, "I can love others!"
• "Can you find someone praying for others?" Have children name someone they pray about and how they ask Heavenly Father to help that person.
• "Can you find anyone who helps do work around the yard?" Have children tell you how they help in the yard (e.g., pulling weeds, picking flowers or vegetables, finding and caring for ladybugs and potato bugs).
• "Can you find someone who shares a loving hug?" Have children tell you why they like hugs and whom they give hugs to.
• "Can you find a boy giving some flowers to a lonely neighbor?" Ask children to tell you someone they visit who is lonely and needs a friend.

3. <u>Talk about the Home Activity</u>: "Help me look for ways to be kind like Jesus. Show me how to speak kindly to everyone. Help me so I can also say please, thank you, I'm sorry, and excuse me."

THOUGHT TREAT: All-kinds-of-kindness necklace. String cereal on ribbon for a necklace, talking about ways to be kind and show others love as children eat each piece from their necklace.

GOOD SAMARITAN STORY – Luke 10:33-34

Jesus told a man how to get to heaven as He told a story.
A man was lying on the road, hurt.
A man saw him and did not stop to help.
A second man saw him and did not stop to help.
Then a Samaritan man stopped to help this poor man.
He gave him water to drink. He put clothes on the man.
He took him to an inn. He gave him money.
Jesus wants us to be kind to others and help them.

Can you find someone praying for others?

Can you find someone sharing a loving hug?

I can love others!

Can you find anyone helping do work around the yard?

Can you find a boy giving some flowers to a lonely neighbor?

Home Activity: Help me look for ways to be kind like Jesus. Show me how to speak kindly to everyone. Help me so I can also say please, thank you, I'm sorry, and excuse me.

LESSON 35 THEME: I Can Be Kind to Animals

1. Present lesson on p. 115–118 in the *Primary 1 Sunbeam* manual to help children understand the importance of being kind to animals.
2. Present both or one of the following activities to help teach the lesson visually.
3. Sing with children. Sing "Jesus Said Love Everyone" (*Children's Songbook*, 61). For fun visuals, go to the same song in the *Super Little Singers* book (62) or CD-ROM.

Activity 69 – Serving Animals
Cat and Dog Spoon

1. Copy the spoons that follow for each child. Glue spoons back to back.
2. The spoon has a cute description of a cat and dog and shows ways children can take care of their pets.
Fun Option: Tie a regular dog bone biscuit around the middle of spoon and tell child to take it home to feed their dog or ask a friend's parents if you can give it to their dog.

THOUGHT TREAT: Dog bone cookie. Roll and cut out sugar cookie or gingerbread dough into dog bone shapes. Bake at 350° for 8–10 minutes.
Note: Tell child not to feed dog bone cookies to their dogs because pets should not eat sweets.

Activity 70 – Kind to Animals Poster

1. Copy the poster that follows for each child to color.
2. Talk about poster, saying, "I can be kind to animals." Enjoy paw-print activities:
• Have children count the paw prints on the handout with you.
• Have children make paw prints like those on the handout, using their hands (placing thumb for large part of paw and fingertips for the rest). This can be done with pudding on waxed paper (they can eat the prints), or on paper using poster paint (washing hands after).
• Have them tell you why they like their pets and love to see their paw prints.
3. Talk about the Home Activity: "Teach me how to take care of my pets and to not forget that they need food, water, exercise, play, and lots of love."

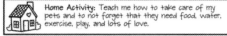

THOUGHT TREAT: Kitty's milk. Children can drink a glass of milk (check for allergies ahead of time, buying rice or soy milk if necessary). Talk about how kittens love to lick up a bowl of milk (as shown on visual) and how they drink their milk differently than we do. Tell about kittens and other animals and how we should treat them. Explain how hungry our pets can get if we forget to feed them.

DOGS
you
know
can
be a
best
friend.

Pet
Care
___
Feed,
water,
run, and
wrestle!

COOKIE PATTERN

CATS
lick
and
purr
purr
till the
day's
end!

Pet
Care
___
Feed,
water,
and tease
with a
string.

I can be kind to animals.

 **Home Activity:** Teach me how to take care of my pets and to not forget that they need food, water, exercise, play, and lots of love.

LESSON 36 THEME: I Can Be a Good Example

1. Present lesson on p. 119–121 in the *Primary 1 Sunbeam* manual to help children learn to set a good example to others by following the example of Jesus.

2. Present both or one of the following activities to help teach the lesson visually.

3. Sing with children. Sing "Jesus Said Love Everyone" (*Children's Songbook*, 61). For fun visuals, go to the same song in the *Super Little Singers* book (62) or CD-ROM. Sing "Jesus Once Was a Little Child," (*Children's Songbook*, 55).

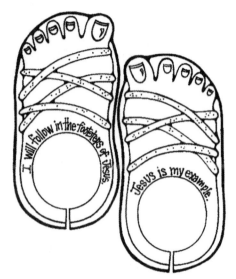

Activity 71 – Follow in Jesus's Steps – Example Sandals

1. Copy the sandal feet that follow for each child and cut out.

2. Children can wear Example Sandals over their shoes/around ankles to remind them to follow in the footsteps of Jesus. Place double-stick tape between sandal and shoe to keep on.

THOUGHT TREAT: Footprint cookie. Roll sugar cookie dough into two-inch balls. Make imprint in dough with side of fist. Press with fingers at the top to make toes. To color toenails, mix food coloring with sugar in the bottle and shake well. Sprinkle on toes, or mix 1 teaspoon of canned milk with food coloring and paint toes. Bake at 350° for 8–10 minutes.

Activity 72 – Jesus's Example Poster

1. Copy the poster that follows for each child to color.

2. Talk about poster, saying, "I can be an example. I want to be like Jesus. I will follow Him."

• Jesus showed us how to love and be kind to everyone. Talk about Jesus serving others and about Jesus washing His Apostles' feet (JST John 13:8, 10). Show gospel art picture from ward library (GAK 226).

3. Talk about the Home Activity: "Help me know when I am being a good example. I am happy when I am kind, loving, and choosing the right. Help me be more like Jesus."

Home Activity: Help me know when I am being a good example. I am happy when I am kind, loving, and choosing the right. Help me be more like Jesus.

THOUGHT TREAT: Footstep fudge. Make fudge by microwaving one-half can sweetened condensed milk and one bag of semi-sweet chocolate chips for 2-4 minutes. Stir fudge and form into feet shapes. Press tiny candies into fudge for toenails. Tell children that if we follow Jesus, walking in His footsteps, we can show love and be a good example.

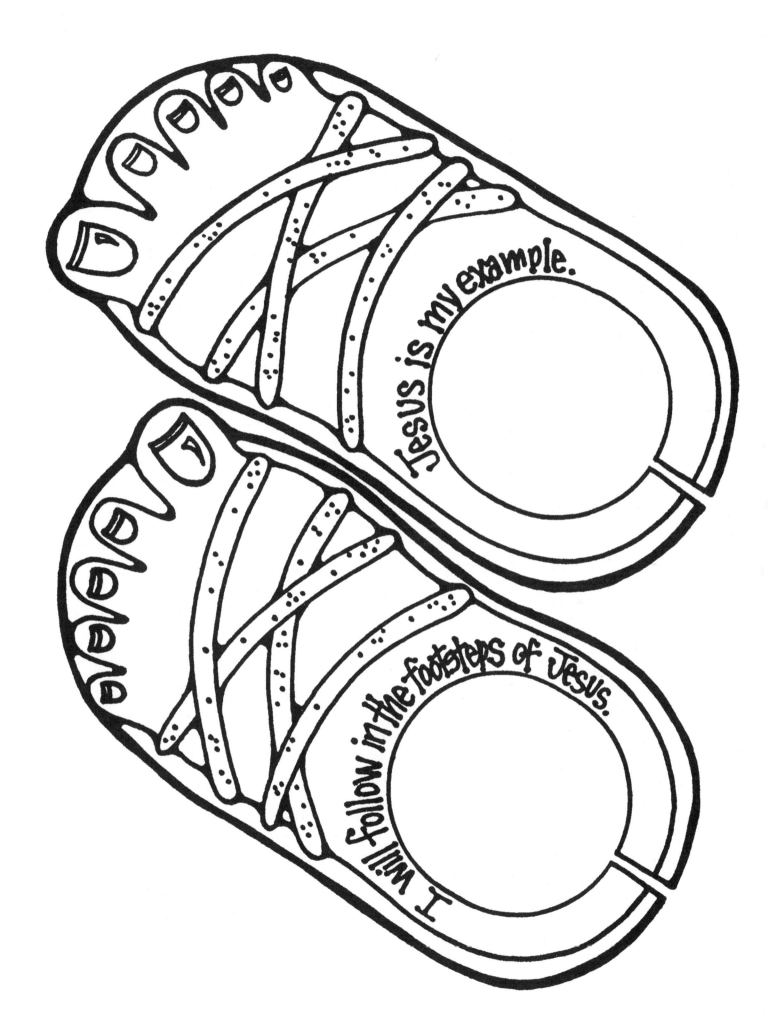

Jesus is my example.

I will follow in the footsteps of Jesus.

I can be an

I want to be like Jesus.

I will follow Him.

example.

Home Activity: Help me know when I am being a good example. I am happy when I am kind, loving, and choosing the right. Help me be more like Jesus.

LESSON 37 THEME: I Can Be Honest

1. Present lesson on p. 122–124 in the *Primary 1 Sunbeam* manual to help strengthen each child's desire to be honest.

2. Present both or one of the following activities to help teach the lesson visually.

3. Sing with children. Sing "Fun to Do" (*Children's Songbook*, 253). For fun visuals, go to the same song in the *Super Little Singers* book (34) or CD-ROM. Children can use the action cards to get started, then sing, "Being honest is fun to do" or "Telling the truth is fun to do."

Activity 73 – I Can Be Honest – Stripling Warrior Headband

1. Copy the headband that follows for each child. Glue warriors on headband left and right where indicated. Fit headband to child's forehead and tape together.

2. This headband will remind children that they can be honest like the stripling warriors. Tell the story found in Alma 53:16–22 and 56:45–57, especially Alma 53:20–21. These men were protected in battle because they were honest. They had faith and courage to do what is right.

Children can wear headbands and march around the room pretending to be righteous warriors, proud and happy that they are honest.

THOUGHT TREAT: Chocolate chip or oatmeal raisin cookies. Place cookies inside a cookie jar and have children say, "May I have a cookie from the cookie jar?" Or, "May I have a cookie please?" Talk about the stripling warriors. They loved their mothers and were honest. We too can be honest and ask for things, like cookies from the cookie jar, rather than just taking them.

Activity 74 – Be Honest Poster

1. Copy the poster that follows for each child to color.

2. Talk about poster, saying, "I can be honest."

• "I will not take things that do not belong to me."
Have a box full of things children like—fish crackers, money (shown on handout), and toys. Say, "These things belong to me, but if you want to have a fish cracker, you can ask me, and I will share it with you. If you want a toy that costs money, you don't take the money from others, but do jobs to earn the money. This is being honest. If you want to play with my toys, you can ask, and I will share them with you. But never take something that doesn't belong to you. That is not honest."

• "I can tell the truth." What if you broke your mother's special dish? Would you hide it and not tell her? No. You would say you are sorry and try not to touch her special things.

3. Talk about the Home Activity: "Let's talk about the qualities of a person that is honest. Help me to never take things that are not mine and to always speak the truth."

THOUGHT TREAT: Truthful trout (goldfish crackers). Tell children stories about honesty or dishonesty. As children hear an honest action they can say, "Truthful Trout," and go fish for a cracker.

I can be honest.

I will not take things that do not belong to me.

I will tell the truth!

Home Activity: Let's talk about the qualities of a person who is honest. Help me to never take things that are not mine and to always speak the truth.

LESSON 38   THEME: I Can Be Reverent

1. Present lesson on p. 125–128 in the *Primary 1 Sunbeam* manual to encourage children to show love for Heavenly Father and Jesus Christ by being reverent.

2. Present both or one of the following activities to help teach the lesson visually.

3. Sing with children. Sing "Fun to Do" (*Children's Songbook*, 253). For fun visuals, go to the same song in the *Super Little Singers* book (34) or CD-ROM. Children can use the action cards to get started, then sing, "Being Reverent Is Fun To Do." Then they can show ways to be reverent (e.g., folding arms, closing eyes, sitting quietly, listening, and raising their hand before speaking).

Activity 75 – Reverent at Home & Church – Reverence Racoon Storybook

Copy the book pages that follow for each child to make them a Reverence Racoon storybook. Here, they can learn ways to be reverent and happy at home and church by acting out the reverence actions in story. To make, staple pages together.

THOUGHT TREAT: Marshmallow raccoon eyes. Line a cookie sheet with waxed paper. Place two large marshmallows for each child on a tray. Melt marshmallows until light brown. Remove from oven and place a small gumdrop or round candy piece in the center for the eye. Tell children that these look like the eyes of a reverent raccoon. He can see each one of you being reverent.

Activity 76 – Reverence Poster

1. Copy the poster that follows for each child to color.

2. <u>Talk about poster</u>, saying, "I can be reverent."
Play follow the leader, showing children reverent actions (see Thought Treat below). Children can take turns being the leader as others follow. Talk about what each reverent action means to those who are trying to listen and learn about Jesus and Heavenly Father.

3. <u>Talk about the Home Activity</u>: "Help me be reverent in family home evening and during family prayer. Help me learn to be reverent in church by bringing something quiet to do."

THOUGHT TREAT: Hands, feet, eyes, and mouth crackers. Use a can of spray cheese to draw these images onto four soda crackers for each child. Talk about our body and how we can keep it reverent to show love for Heavenly Father and Jesus. *Reverent Actions:* raise your hand before speaking, keep your arms folded during prayer, keep your hands and feet still during lesson and singing time, walk quietly in Heavenly Father's house, keep your eyes on the teacher or song leader, keep your eyes closed during prayer, keep your mouth singing songs and speaking kind words, take your turn at playing, keep your chair in place, listen and share your ideas, share your toys and treats, say please and thank you.

Reverence Raccoon

Reverence Raccoon was quiet when his family prayed.

He listened at family home evening.

Reverence Racoon walked quietly at church.

He raised his hand before he talked.

Reverence Raccoon folded his arms during the sacrament.

I can be reverent.

Home Activity: Help me be reverent in family home evening and during family prayer. Help me learn to be reverent in church by bringing something quiet I can do.

LESSON 39 THEME: Music Makes Me Happy

1. Present lesson on p. 129–131 in the *Primary 1 Sunbeam* manual to help children understand that good music can help us feel happy and remind us of Heavenly Father and Jesus.

2. Present both or one of the following activities to help teach the lesson visually.

3. Sing with children. Sing "If You're Happy" (*Children's Songbook*, 266). For fun action activity, go to the same song in the *Super Little Singers* book (159) or CD-ROM.

Activity 77 – Happy Music – Band Concert Instruments

1. Copy the song and music labels that follow for each child. To create the tambourine, glue the *Happy Song* label on a paper plate and place rice, popcorn, or beans inside. Place a plate on top, punch holes and sew together with yarn. To create the *Music makes me happy* shaker, place label on one of two cups, insert rice, popcorn, or beans in the bottom of one cup. Tape a second cup to the first. Tie on a few yarn streamers.

2. Use the *Happy Song* tambourine and the *Music makes me happy* shaker to create a band concert. Play music while children shake their tambourine with one hand and shake shaker with the other hand.

3. Sing "Happy Song" (p. 129) in the *Primary 1 Sunbeam* manual. Pictures on tambourine illustrate song.

THOUGHT TREAT: Sunbeam gelatin. Create the lemon-flavored gelatin jigglers recipe. Spray a shallow pan with cooking spray before adding gelatin dessert. Refrigerate three hours to set. Turn firm gelatin onto waxed paper and cut out circles to look like suns. Sing "Jesus Wants Me for a Sunbeam," p. 60 in the *Children's Songbook*.

Activity 78 – I Love Music! Poster

1. Copy the poster that follows for each child to color.

2. Talk about poster, saying, "I love music!"

• Talk about music, the melody that helps us sing the songs. For older children, play "Name that Tune" by having them guess as you hum familiar tunes.

• Strike up a band by making instruments* ahead of time: bang a drum, shake a shaker, or ring bells.

• Use the Stop and Go signs* to direct the band.

• Go Fish with children to choose a song using fish visuals*.

• For great singing and music playing, award children with a colored pencil or singing awards*.

*See *Super Little Singers* book or CD-ROM to make: Band Concert Instruments (p. 161), Stop and Go signs (p. 168, 185-86), Go Fish visuals (p. 163), and Super Singer Awards (p. 168).

3. Talk about the Home Activity: "Let's listen to music together! Help me know what kind of music makes me feel happy and helps me think of Heavenly Father and Jesus."

THOUGHT TREAT: Love-note bread. Using a can of cheese, draw a few heart-shaped love notes (see above) on bread (crust trimmed off). Tell children that these are music notes that tell us how to play a tune. Hum a familiar tune. When we learn the Primary songs, we are listening to good music that makes us feel good.

I Love Music!

Home Activity: Let's listen to music together! Help me know what kind of music makes me feel happy and helps me think of Heavenly Father and Jesus.

LESSON 40   THEME: The Sacrament Helps Me Think About Jesus

1. Present lesson on p. 132–134 in the *Primary 1 Sunbeam* manual to encourage children to think about Jesus Christ during the sacrament.

2. Present both or one of the following activities to help teach the lesson visually.

3. Sing with children. Sing "Jesus Loved the Little Children," "Jesus Said Love Everyone," and "Jesus Wants Me for a Sunbeam" (*Children's Songbook*, 40, 61, 60). For fun visuals, go to the same songs in the *Super Little Singers* book (61-62) or CD-ROM.

Activity 79 – Remembering Jesus – Sacrament Manners Match Game

1. Copy two sets of match game cards that follow for each child.

2. Help children talk about the sacrament and ways to show good manners when we take the sacrament and remember Jesus. Show a picture of Jesus when you do this.

3. *To Play:* Turn cards face down. Take turns turning two cards over to try to make a match. If cards match, keep matching cards. If cards don't match, turn cards back over and next player tries to make a match.

THOUGHT TREAT: Cookies or graham crackers.

Activity 80 – Thinking of Jesus Poster

1. Copy the poster that follows for each child to color.

2. Talk about poster, saying, "I will think about Jesus."

• "I will do my best to sing or listen to the sacrament song." Tell children that the words in the sacrament songs help us think of His love for us. For example, the song "Sacrament" (*Children's Songbook*, 72) helps us think of Jesus giving His life for us. We can thank Him when we take the bread and water.

• "I will listen carefully to the sacrament prayers." Tell children that the sacrament prayers are different from prayers we say to bless the food and to listen to them carefully.

• "I will think about the stories of Jesus during the sacrament." Review story, showing picture (GAK 322) of Jesus blessing the Nephite children (see Luke 18:16; 3 Ne. 17:21–24; He took them one by one and blessed them).

• "I will do my best to always remember Him." Tell children that when we think of Jesus often, we will try to be like Him. This will make us very happy.

3. Talk about the Home Activity: "If I forget to be reverent during the sacrament, remind me to think about Jesus as I take the bread and water."

THOUGHT TREAT: Unleavened bread. Cut a piece of pita bread in fourths and give a piece to each child. Tell them this is the type of bread Jesus gave to His Apostles when He gave them the first sacrament.

to the sacrament prayers. ♡ I will think about the stories of Jesus during the sacrament. ♡ I will do my best to always remember Him.

♡ I will listen carefully to the sacrament song.

♡ I will do my best to sing or listen to the sacrament song.

I Will Think about Jesus

Home Activity: If I forget to be reverent during the sacrament, remind me to think about Jesus as I take the bread and water.

LESSON 41 THEME: Heavenly Father and Jesus Gave Us the Scriptures

1. Present lesson on p. 135–137 in the *Primary 1 Sunbeam* manual to help children understand that the scriptures contain the words of Heavenly Father and Jesus Christ. We can learn of Them by studying the scriptures. As we ponder them, we can receive great joy and peace (2 Nephi 4:15).
2. Present both or one of the following activities to help teach the lesson visually.
3. Sing with children. Sing "Book of Mormon Stories" (*Children's Songbook*, 118). For fun action activities, go to the same song in the *Super Little Singers* book (157) or CD-ROM.

Activity 81 – Scriptures Contain True Stories – Book of Mormon Show-and-Tell

1. Copy the picture story cards that follow for each child. Fold and glue stories on the back of matching picture.
2. Use the cards to help children learn the following true stories of six Book of Mormon heroes: Nephi, Abinadi, Alma, Ammon, Captain Moroni, and the three Nephites.

THOUGHT TREAT: "Picture this" cookie. Provide a cookie children can draw/frost a picture of their favorite Book of Mormon scripture story figure (e.g., Nephi on ship, going to Promised Land). Tell a scripture story as they munch.

Activity 82 – Scriptures Poster

1. Copy the poster that follows for each child to color.
2. <u>Talk about poster</u>, saying, "I love the scriptures!"
• Tell a story from each book of scripture. For example, in the Book of Mormon in 1 Nephi, tell of the prophet Lehi, who is told to take his family and flee into the wilderness because Jerusalem will be destroyed. His family is led to the Promised Land by a compass that works only when the family obeys God (Alma 37:44).
3. <u>Talk about the Home Activity</u>: "Let's read the scriptures together! Help me love the scriptures by reading them with me. Help me understand the stories we read."

THOUGHT TREAT: Iron rod—licorice or pretzel. Give children a string of licorice or a pretzel stick. Talk about the iron rod told about in Lehi's dream (1 Nephi 8:19) that helps us stay on the strait path. The iron rod is the word of God found in the scriptures.

Nephi

I had faith that I could return to Jerusalem to get the brass plates. These were sacred records kept by the prophets.

Abinadi

Because of my faith in Jesus Christ, I was willing to die for my testimony (at the hands of King Noah).

Captain Moroni

I used the title of Liberty flag to encourage my people to have faith in Jesus Christ and fight for liberty.

Three Nephites

Because of our faith in Jesus Christ, we were promised we shall never face death.

Alma

Because of my faith and prayers, an angel appeared to my son and the four sons of Mosiah, calling them to repentence.

Ammon

I desired to preach the gospel of Jesus Christ. My faith helped me fight a band of robbers who were trying to kill King Lamoni's sheep.

I love the scriptures!

Home Activity: Let's read the scriptures together! Help me love the scriptures by reading them with me. Help me understand the stories we read.

LESSON 42   THEME: I Belong to The Church of Jesus Christ of Latter-day Saints

1. Present lesson on p. 138–141 in the *Primary 1 Sunbeam* manual to help children understand that they belong to The Church of Jesus Christ of Latter-day Saints.

2. Present both or one of the following activities to help teach the lesson visually.

3. Sing with children. Sing "The Church of Jesus Christ," "I Am Like a Star," and "Jesus Wants Me for a Sunbeam" (*Children's Songbook*, 77, 163, 60). For fun visuals, go to the same songs in the *Super Little Singers* book (61, 62) or CD-ROM.

Activity 83 – I Can Do Many Things at Church! – Church Charm Bracelet

1. Copy the church charms that follow for each child. To make the Church charm bracelet, punch holes in the charms and thread string through each, tying a knot between each to separate. Tie a knot at the end to slip onto child's wrist.

2. Charms on bracelet show children the many things they can do at church to show good behavior. Show each picture and talk about the actions. Example: Eye ("read scripture stories"), Hand ("play kindly with friends"), Ear ("listen carefully to teachers"), and Mouth ("speak softly while in church").

THOUGHT TREAT: Doll cookie. Cut out a gingerbread cookie girl and boy. Frost cookie after baking, or paint with cookie paints before baking. To make cookie paints, mix two teaspoons canned milk with food coloring. Spread on cookie dough with paint brush. As children eat cookie, talk about the eyes, hands, ears, and mouth that help us do many things at Church.

Activity 84 – I Belong to the Church Poster

1. Copy the poster that follows for each child to color.

2. <u>Talk about poster</u>, saying, "I belong to The Church of Jesus Christ of Latter-day Saints."

• "Priesthood": Worthy men in the Church hold a special power from God to heal and bless the sick, baptize, and give us the gift of the Holy Ghost.

• "Living Prophets": Ask children, "Who is the living prophet leading Jesus Christ's Church today?" Talk about him and share something he has said (see *Friend* magazine).

• "Scriptures": Tell children that the scriptures teach us where we came from, why we are here on earth, and how to choose the right so we can live in heaven again someday.

3. <u>Talk about the Home Activity</u>: "Let's talk about what it means to be a member of the Church. Help me understand that we have the priesthood, a living prophet, and the scriptures that teach us truth."

THOUGHT TREAT: Me-a-member cookie. Give children a gingerbread man (cookie). Talk about how they can stand up tall as a member of The Church of Jesus Christ of Latter-day Saints. Have children stand tall and hold up their cookie before eating it. Sing, "The Church of Jesus Christ."

Living Prophets

Priesthood

Scriptures

I Belong to
The Church of Jesus Christ
of Latter-day Saints

Home Activity: Let's talk about what it means to be a member of the Church. Help me understand that we have the priesthood, a living prophet, and the scriptures that teach us truth.

LESSON 43 THEME: We Have a Living Prophet

1. Present lesson on p. 142–144 in the *Primary 1 Sunbeam* manual to help children understand that we are blessed when we follow the prophet.

2. Present both or one of the following activities to help teach the lesson visually.

3. Sing with children. Sing "Do As I'm Doing" (*Children's Songbook*, 276). For fun visuals, go to the same song in the *Super Little Singers* book (2) or CD-ROM. After singing the song the first time, sing "Follow the prophet, follow, follow me." Then sing things children can do to follow the prophet (e.g., choose the right, go to church, obey mother and father, help brothers and sisters, be kind to others). Then sing the words "follow, follow me."

Activity 85 – Blessed from Following the Prophet – Prophet Fold-out

1. Copy the fold-out poster that follows for each child. Fold and tape pictures together as shown.

2. With this poster, children can show and tell about the prophets who talk to Heavenly Father and Jesus. Poster can remind children they are blessed when they follow the prophet. Talk about why they will be blessed.

THOUGHT TREAT: Prophet punch. In small cups, pour each child some punch and say, "The prophet brings us many blessings. As we sip our punch, let's talk about each prophet we have learned about."

Activity 86 – Prophet Poster

1. Copy the poster that follows for each child to color.

2. Talk about poster, saying, "Follow the prophet! Like those who followed Noah, Moses, and Joseph Smith, we are blessed when we follow the prophet."

• Tell about the prophets on the handout: Noah, who built a boat to save his family and two of every animal from the flood; Moses, who went to a high mountain and received from Jesus Christ the Ten Commandments written in stone; Joseph Smith, who was led to the golden plates hidden in a hill and who later translated these records into the Book of Mormon (he also restored Jesus's Church so we could have the gospel today); the current prophet (read something he has written from the *Friend*, or tell what he has done).

3. Talk about the Home Activity: "Let's talk about our prophet today. Tell me stories about our prophet, and let's read about what he has said. Let's hang his picture so we can remember what he has asked us to do."

THOUGHT TREAT: Prophet blessings bag. Have a bag filled with assorted cereal children can choose from as you talk about following the prophet. Have children come up and say one way they can follow the prophet as they choose a piece of cereal. Leader can name a blessing for following each action.

My
PROPHET
POSTER

We are blessed
when we follow
the prophet.

Nephi

Noah

Joseph Smith

Moses

Draw Today's Prophet

Like those who followed the prophet Noah, Moses, and Joseph Smith, we are blessed when we follow the prophet.

Follow the prophet!

Home Activity: Let's talk about our prophet today. Tell me stories about our prophet, and let's read about what he has said. Let's hang his picture so we can remember what he has asked us to do.

LESSON 44   THEME: We Can All Help at Church

1. Present lesson on p. 145–147 in the *Primary 1 Sunbeam* manual to help children understand that every member of the ward or branch can help at church.

2. Present both or one of the following activities to help teach the lesson visually.

3. Sing with children. Sing "When We're Helping" and "Jesus Wants Me for a Sunbeam" (*Children's Songbook*, 198, 60). For fun visuals, go to the same song in the *Super Little Singers* book (132, 62) or CD-ROM.

Activity 87 – The Bishop Helps Me – Bishop Brag Bag

1. Copy the brag bag label and brag cards that follow for each child. After cutting out, enclose label and pictures in bag as shown. Make an extra bag for the bishop.

2. Talk about the brag cards, telling how the bishop helps at church.

3. Also slip treats into the bag (see below).

4. Plan ahead that after the lesson activity, children can go see the bishop in his office to deliver the Bishop brag bag and present the ideas to him personally.

THOUGHT TREAT: "Bear-y gurr-ate" brag bag goodies. Place miniature bear cookies or cinnamon or gummy bear candies in Bishop brag bag.

Activity 88 – Help at Church Poster

1. Copy the poster that follows for each child to color.

2. Talk about poster, saying, "I can help at church!"

• "I can walk reverently in church." Demonstrate the right way to walk through the meetinghouse.

• "I can pick up trash from around my chair." Talk about how the church is Heavenly Father's house. If we leave a mess or don't pick up messes others leave, we are not showing love and respect for Heavenly Father and Jesus.

• "I can thank my teacher for such wonderful lessons." Have a child help you give part of the lesson, then thank him or her for helping tell others about the gospel. Ask children to thank the child for helping you.

• "I can say the prayer when asked." Ask children to volunteer to say the prayer, telling them that you will help them. Ask, "When we pray, whom do we pray to?" "What do we say?" Review the lesson 4 handout.

3. Talk about the Home Activity: "Help me realize we can all help at church. I can be helpful, reverent, and remember to say thank you to those who have helped me."

THOUGHT TREAT: Fishers-of-men crackers. Place a picture of a fish on three or four pictures of Jesus. Give children goldfish crackers to munch on as you have each child come up and choose a picture with a fish attached. Tell the story. Tell children that Jesus asked His disciples to be fishers of men, to bring in and teach those who want to hear the gospel. Talk about how we can be fishers of men by helping at church. Name ways (e.g., being reverent so others can hear the stories of Jesus).

Bishop Brag Bag

Receives revelation

Conducts meetings

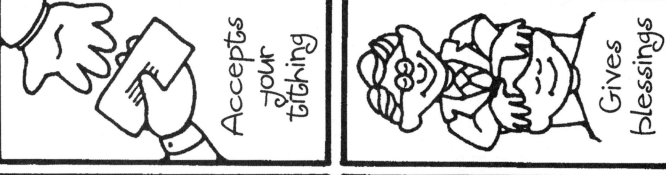

Accepts your tithing

Gives blessings

Visits the sick

Teaches the gospel

I can help at church!

I can walk reverently in church. I can pick up trash from around my chair. I can thank my teacher for such wonderful lessons. I can say the prayer when asked.

Home Activity: Help me realize we can all help at church. I can be helpful, reverent, and remember to say thank you to those who have helped me.

LESSON 45 THEME: The Resurrection of Jesus Christ (Easter)

1. Present lesson on p. 148–150 in the *Primary 1 Sunbeam* manual to help children understand that Jesus Christ was resurrected.

2. Present both or one of the following activities to help teach the lesson visually.

3. Sing with children. Sing "I Am a Child of God" and "Jesus Loved the Little Children" (*Children's Songbook*, 2, 59). For fun visuals, go to the same songs in the *Super Little Singers* book (34, 61) or CD-ROM.

Activity 89 – Jesus Loves Me – Resurrection Book

1. Copy the book pages that follow for each child. Assemble and bend tab at top and glue or staple pages together.

2. Children can review this Jesus loves me book to spotlight the life of Jesus and remind them of the things He did to show His love for us.

THOUGHT TREAT: New beginning basket.
Idea 1: Make an Easter basket using a small round bowl for the mold with Rice Krispies recipe (on box of Kellogg's cereal).
Idea 2: Make a nest using bread dough and bake. Fill basket with candy eggs and tell children that baby birds come from eggs. They are hatched in the springtime. This is the time Jesus died and was resurrected. When we see these eggs, let's remember Jesus and that he loves us.

Activity 90 – Resurrection Poster

1. Copy the poster that follows for each child to color.
2. Talk about poster, saying, "Jesus lives again! Because Jesus was resurrected, we will also live again."

• Review with children the story of the Resurrection. Tell them that because of Jesus, everyone will receive a new body. This will start to happen when Jesus comes again. When it is time, those who are dead will live again.

• Bear your testimony of Jesus and His power to bring life to the earth. Say that we can trust and believe in Him. Read John 11:25: "Jesus said . . . I am the resurrection, and the life: he that believeth in me, though he were dead, yet shall he live."

3. Talk about the Home Activity: "Help me understand that because Jesus was resurrected, we will all be resurrected someday. Tell me why you are grateful for Jesus."

 Home Activity: Help me understand that because Jesus was resurrected, we will all be resurrected someday. Tell me why you are grateful for Jesus.

THOUGHT TREAT: Easter eggs. Give each child a hard-boiled, colored Easter egg. Explain that an Easter basket filled with eggs means a new beginning (baby chicks or birds are born, hatched from eggs). Jesus brought the world a new beginning when He was resurrected. He promised that we will all be resurrected again—that we will all have a new body one day.

Jesus loves me.

Jesus came to earth to show the way.

Jesus showed me how to be baptized.

Jesus taught me how to pray.

Jesus showed me how to care for others.

Jesus showed me how to love.

Jesus died for me.

Jesus was resurrected so I can live again.

Jesus lives again!

Because Jesus was resurrected, we will also live again.

Home Activity: Help me understand that because Jesus was resurrected, we will all be resurrected someday. Tell me why you are grateful for Jesus.

LESSON 46 THEME: The Birth of Jesus Christ (Christmas)

1. Present lesson on p. 151–153 in the *Sunbeam Primary 1* manual to help children feel gratitude for the birth of Jesus Christ.

2. Present both or one of the following activities to help teach the lesson visually.

3. Sing with children. Sing "Away in a Manger" and "Jesus Loved the Little Children" (*Children's Songbook*, 42, 59). For fun action activities, go to the same song in the *Super Little Singers* book (157, 61) or CD-ROM.

Activity 91 – My Gift to Jesus Is to Be like Him – Kind Deeds Advent Necklace

1. Copy the advent circles and parents' note that follows for each child. Punch holes in circles and slip yarn through as shown to slip around child's neck.

2. Place twelve gold stars in a plastic bag for each child. Then attach the parents' note to the bag so they will know what to do with the gold stars—placing them on the child's forehead or on the corresponding circle for kind deeds done.

3. This Kind Deeds advent necklace will remind children of kind deeds they can do each day for twelve days before Christmas.

THOUGHT TREAT: Star cookies (see below).

Activity 92 – Baby Jesus Poster

1. Give children the poster to color.

2. Talk about poster, saying, "I'm thankful for Jesus's birth."

• Tell the story of the birth of Jesus. Show the lesson 5 handout, which says that Jesus Christ is the Son of Heavenly Father.

• Talk about the birth of baby Jesus, telling of the shepherds who followed the special star that shown bright that night, leading them to the baby Jesus. They found Him in a manger with Mary and Joseph. The wise men also came and brought gifts of gold, frankincense, and myrrh.

• *See Stars on Handout:* Read, "What gifts can I give Him?" We can learn to do many things. We can serve others, we can learn to help at home, be kind, share, and care. Read, "How can I show my love?" We can be kind to others, and this way we are being kind to Jesus. He was born on the earth so He could grow up and teach us how to be happy and love others.

3. Talk about the Home Activity: "Tell me about the special night that Jesus was born and what gifts I can give to Him."

THOUGHT TREAT: Star cookies. Frost star-shaped cookies. Tell children about that special star that was brighter than all the stars in the sky that night, leading the shepherds to Jesus.

Dear Parents:

Your child is wearing a Kind Deeds Advent necklace. Please place a star on the circle or on the child's forehead for each kind deed your child has done. These kind deeds are your child's gift to Jesus, and the stars represent the star of Bethlehem.

Dear Parents:

Your child is wearing a Kind Deeds Advent necklace. Please place a star on the circle or on the child's forehead for each kind deed your child has done. These kind deeds are your child's gift to Jesus, and the stars represent the star of Bethlehem.

Dear Parents:

Your child is wearing a Kind Deeds Advent necklace. Please place a star on the circle or on the child's forehead for each kind deed your child has done. These kind deeds are your child's gift to Jesus, and the stars represent the star of Bethlehem.

Dear Parents:

Your child is wearing a Kind Deeds Advent necklace. Please place a star on the circle or on the child's forehead for each kind deed your child has done. These kind deeds are your child's gift to Jesus, and the stars represent the star of Bethlehem.

Dear Parents:

Your child is wearing a Kind Deeds Advent necklace. Please place a star on the circle or on the child's forehead for each kind deed your child has done. These kind deeds are your child's gift to Jesus, and the stars represent the star of Bethlehem.

Dear Parents:

Your child is wearing a Kind Deeds Advent necklace. Please place a star on the circle or on the child's forehead for each kind deed your child has done. These kind deeds are your child's gift to Jesus, and the stars represent the star of Bethlehem.

Dear Parents:

Your child is wearing a Kind Deeds Advent necklace. Please place a star on the circle or on the child's forehead for each kind deed your child has done. These kind deeds are your child's gift to Jesus, and the stars represent the star of Bethlehem.

Dear Parents:

Your child is wearing a Kind Deeds Advent necklace. Please place a star on the circle or on the child's forehead for each kind deed your child has done. These kind deeds are your child's gift to Jesus, and the stars represent the star of Bethlehem.

Dear Parents:

Your child is wearing a Kind Deeds Advent necklace. Please place a star on the circle or on the child's forehead for each kind deed your child has done. These kind deeds are your child's gift to Jesus, and the stars represent the star of Bethlehem.

Dear Parents:

Your child is wearing a Kind Deeds Advent necklace. Please place a star on the circle or on the child's forehead for each kind deed your child has done. These kind deeds are your child's gift to Jesus, and the stars represent the star of Bethlehem.

Dear Parents:

Your child is wearing a Kind Deeds Advent necklace. Please place a star on the circle or on the child's forehead for each kind deed your child has done. These kind deeds are your child's gift to Jesus, and the stars represent the star of Bethlehem.

Dear Parents:

Your child is wearing a Kind Deeds Advent necklace. Please place a star on the circle or on the child's forehead for each kind deed your child has done. These kind deeds are your child's gift to Jesus, and the stars represent the star of Bethlehem.

What gifts can I give Him?

How can I show my love?

I'm thankful for Jesus's birth.

Home Activity: Tell me about the special night that Jesus was born and what gifts I can give to Him.

Sunny Sunday Sack

Show-and-Tell Pocket

There is shine in my heart.

I am a child of God!

Show-and-Tell Pocket

I am a child of God!

I am a child of God!

My Heavenly Father loves me!

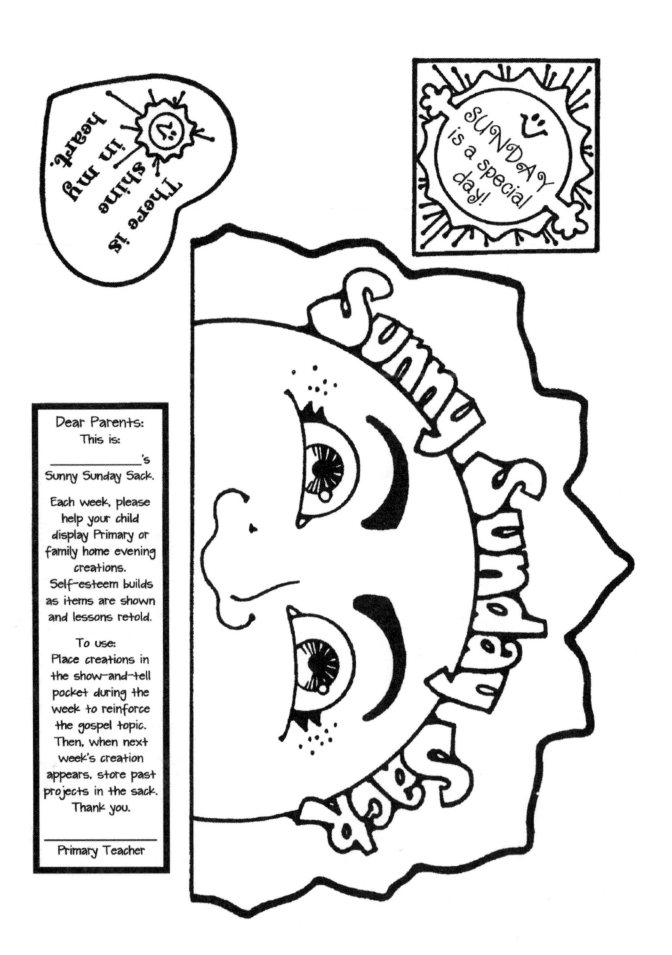

There is shine in my heart.

SUNDAY is a special day!

Sunny Sunday Sack

Dear Parents:
This is:

_____'s
Sunny Sunday Sack.

Each week, please help your child display Primary or family home evening creations. Self-esteem builds as items are shown and lessons retold.

To use:
Place creations in the show-and-tell pocket during the week to reinforce the gospel topic. Then, when next week's creation appears, store past projects in the sack. Thank you.

_____
Primary Teacher